For Asrar Alam my husband, ⟨
Shoaib and Easha, and especi⟨ y ⟩ ..... daughter Sara
and her partner Fran who moved back home to help
with my younger teenagers Shoaib and Easha while I
commenced my overseas volunteer work.

Thank you to each one of you for being an inspiration for
hard work and dedication; thanks to our family ethos of
'never give up'.

Thank you to Sara Alam

Illustrations dedicatedly, craftily and inspirationally drawn.

Acknowledgements

For seeing my potential for overseas volunteer midwifery work and posting me twice to Uganda as part of the Global Midwifery Twinning Project (GMTP) with DFID funding, I thank the Royal College of Midwives (RCM), the Ugandan Christian University (UCU) midwifery teaching team and students; Aga Khan University School of Nursing and Midwifery (AKU SONAM), but specifically Professor Rafat Jan, also president of the Midwifery Association of Pakistan who bravely invited me out in the capacity of 'visiting faculty' to support midwifery degree students and the professional development of the midwifery faculty. Thank you to all the midwifery students and trainers that made me feel so welcome.

Gillian Duffy Midwifery Director, Hilary Thomas Midwifery Matron and Susan Powley Lead Midwife for supporting and agreeing my two year sabbatical from my midwifery contract post at Maidstone and Tunbridge Wells NHS Trust, allowing me time to study international midwifery and birthing mothers' needs with the aim of reducing the numbers of maternal and infant deaths.

To Middlesex University (MDX) London Institute for Work-Based Learning (WBL) Studies department, specifically Professor Carol Costley Director, Dr Barbara Workman and Dr Margaret Volante for awarding and supporting me with a PhD scholarship and continuing to support my international midwifery teacher's work-based teaching and learning strategies project.

To the Wellbeing of Women (WOW) charity for awarding me the International Fellowship Award (IFA) that helped to finance some of my project and publication expenses. Also thank you again to Professor Rafat Jan at AKU SO-NAM and Barbara Workman MDX WBL for supporting my WOW IFA application: see information about WOW in this book.

Thank you to reviewers who particularly gave extensive comments that helped with the near-finished manuscript: Emma Morris NHS midwife, neonatal life-support trainer, lactation consultant and overseas midwifery volunteer; Bushra Rahman one of Pakistan's first ever midwifery degree graduates from AKU SONAM in December 2014, now based in Lahore Pakistan; Professor Rafat Jan and Rozina Sewani an educationalist, who collectively gave comments and advice; and of course my MTW midwife colleague Merja Hart too for her insightful comments and suggestions.

For being a true pedagogical midwife, I want to thank Mindy Gibbins-Klein from The Book Midwife® who has been with me each step of the way, encouraging me, inspiring me to deliver this book; truly allowing my thoughts and experiences to be born in their own natural way for me.

Finally I want to thank every midwife, mother and student I have worked with and supported, for allowing me the privilege of being with you in your own individual transition journey that continually guides my own transition journeys too.

Contents

Introduction

I am a midwife, teacher and researcher and I am passionate about work-based learning. I have been thinking about how midwifery skills are taught for at least 30 years. Various programmes and experiential learning along the way have consolidated the idea for me that there is no better way to learn how to do something than learning by doing.

It is not a new idea, certainly not my idea. My colleagues will tell you that when I am with a student I become animated and excited, instilling belief and passion in the students too; I want to show them and in turn they show me.

I have mentored midwifery students and obstetric placement student doctors and supervised qualified midwives in their mentoring roles both abroad and at home – it is a wonder it took so long for me to write this book! I have worked with some fantastic and energetic midwifery faculty who are indeed very knowledgeable but are hungry for how to teach 'how to do strategies' and be authentic as they engage with advanced training for midwives and midwife trainers.

There are many instruction manuals for midwifery and teaching written in strict academic style that I felt didn't speak individually to students and teachers that would inspire passion and real ownership for how midwifery is taught and practised especially in developing countries. Put this aspect together with the dire need for more midwives. Sixty per cent of mothers in developing countries birth their babies alone without a skilled birth attendant with them. That is staggering. There is no data for how many student midwives do not have a skilled midwifery teacher in attendance with them as there is such confusion with the term nurse midwife. I have met very experienced midwife teachers but more often than not they are predominantly nurse trainers that have been included as midwifery teachers because there just aren't that many experienced midwife instructors.

When I work with them they want to learn how to undertake midwifery-led care, they want to teach midwifery-led care; huge obstacles prevent this being realised but the hunger and passion is certainly there. Too often I would say: 'students will not know "how" just because you told them'. You will see I have used many different terms for teachers of midwifery but be reassured that if you are with a student – in whatever particular capacity – you are facilitating their learning, so you will see different terms used because they exist and mean different things in different settings, but essentially they are facilitating roles.

Now, about this book; I thought I would write a long letter sharing my knowledge and experience with some of the midwifery facilitators I came into contact with. I asked them what, if I were to write such a letter, they would like to read. This added a few more ideas to the ones that I thought were essential and I had to start writing.

Undertaking a Masters in work-based learning (WBL) and now a PhD in WBL further ignited my need to write. I felt

I needed guidance in how to write a book, so I sought out another type of midwife, Mindy, as I call the pedagogical midwife facilitating me to birth my book; a classic example of how facilitators should be with the student/participant supporting their needs. So I joined a weekend retreat with other aspiring authors and was shown how to create maps to get my ideas out in graphic form and later to just write as the maps I had drawn guided me. I felt alive, empowered and a sense of possibly really helping global midwifery teachers – and ultimately global mothers – to safer care and outcomes.

However, the book has been a journey; I have taught much and learnt a lot. Even after the book is on shelves my learning journey will continue and I hope yours will too. This book is for you, midwife and midwife teachers, trainers, instructors, mentors, supervisors, coaches – the list is just endless. If you are with a student of maternity, or indeed facilitating mothers and family regarding maternity matters, this book is for you.

Chapter 1

Remember: it's a privilege to be there

As a midwife I have always felt it a privilege to be with women at a very special time in their lives. Remember the feeling of supporting and facilitating a woman through hours of her body's *transition from womanhood to motherhood*, encouraging and empowering her to believe that her body and mind are capable of this normal physiological process.

It is a privilege to be there to facilitate this auspicious transition, paying acute attention to supporting her body's normal function and having the skills to recognise when intervention is needed. It is important to intervene at the right time, so as not to interrupt the normal process by premature intervention; to know when and how to seek urgent medical assistance when the labouring process deviates from normal.

I am continually amazed at the power of a woman to give birth, the way her body is designed exactly to fulfil this purpose, from her decisions and belief in herself and the way the physiology of birthing unfolds.

However, for many women throughout the world, they have little say in the decision to birth or not and the physiology is so interfered with that the miracle of birth gets obscured to the point where 'the woman has been delivered by a health care professional'.

Mirror this with the natural process of learning; as a midwife – facilitator of birth and a facilitator of learning – I also consider it a privilege to be with a learner in their transition from novice to expert – a student, too, is on a transformation journey. A midwifery student is learning to be 'with woman' and the role of the midwife teacher is as a facilitator who is 'with student with woman'. The learner often knows what it is they need to learn but find themselves on a pathway that is dictated by curriculum designers that pigeonhole them into a structure that supposedly augments their learning; and at the end of the scripted programme the curriculum designers award them a certificate, claiming that the educational institution has trained them!

This book is about giving power back to the learner in the same way that we should be giving power back to women to be in charge of their bodies. Where we, as facilitators of learning, are, in effect, their assistants not their dictators. When you remember that it is a privilege to be there, you rebalance the power base back to the women and the learner.

As you ponder on this enormous privilege, consider the reality today, the contradiction where women throughout the world suffer incredibly at the hands of untrained or inadequately trained health care workers or even highly trained medical practitioners that advocate a surgical birthing process without even giving nature a chance when there are no complications. Consider for example: in some developing countries sixty per cent of women give birth without a skilled birth attendant – that is a staggering figure. Dwell on it a moment so it becomes real; I am talking more than a million women in one country alone in one year.

I recommend that you visit the website of the 'state of the world's midwifery' (www.sowm.com) and weep at the statistics. Delve into a book entitled *Where Have All the Mothers Gone?* written by a pioneering obstetrician teaching leadership while working in Africa. In this book she describes multiple stories of the reality of the struggle to survive for many women in the Middle East and Africa. So wake up to the reality of these statistics.

'We need more midwives indeed' is the slogan of the International Confederation of Midwives (ICM). However, who is going to train these midwives? Surely we need more midwifery teachers first, a point which funding agencies do not give adequate attention to. Without specific midwifery teachers, what has happened is a surge in the augmented procurement of midwives, fast-tracked 'syntocinon-style' (a man-made drug to 'manage' a speedy chemical birthing process), fulfilling the number demanded.

The deployment into these areas of midwives who have been inducted in theory has justifiably led to the question: 'are skilled birth attendants really skilled?'. I would argue here that you should not augment learning en masse any more than we should be augmenting normal birth en masse. Learning itself is a physiological process for the mind and body.

A skilled facilitator of learning understands these normal learning processes, nurtures and guides them with acute attention and only intervenes with appropriate pedagogical means when this process is struggling. Most importantly they know how and when to intervene. An inadequately trained facilitator of learning can damage the student's motivation and learning progress, resulting in practitioners who are ill-prepared for the realities of life. Consider that an inadequately trained professional may actually increase mortality and morbidity rates not reduce them. The world has woken up to the degradation and inhumanity that many women giving birth face today and targets have been set for all countries of the world to enhance the status of women and reduce infant and maternal mortality.

This book is for facilitators of midwifery training and this is their opportunity to take a close look at the Millennium Development Goals (MDG). There are eight in total: Goal 3 is to promote gender equality and empower women; Goal 4 to reduce child mortality; and Goal 5 to improve maternal health. These goals were set and agreed by all the world's countries, and are not being met, even in 2015.

In my opinion, of one of the reasons why these goals are not being met is the lack of adequately trained midwifery teachers. Ask yourself what will be your role; take respon-sibility and be accountable for this privilege of 'being with student with woman'. What you teach will influence how midwifery is practised – the potential to help or harm is huge. Think about the equipment you use to facilitate learning for the midwifery student. I have observed rough handling of simulators/manikins being exactly demonstrated on real women in clinical settings across the UK, Asia and Africa.

The problem begins with the inappropriate use of resources; for example, simulators/manikins having only the torso, i.e. without a head, or real persons/actors in attendance with atrocious communications skills, both of which could later result in the woman being treated as non-human! The role of the midwife facilitator/teacher as in midwifery faculty is parallel to 'being with woman and with student'. The midwife faculty/teacher is the custodian of the learning experience for the student just as the midwife is the custodian of the birthing experience for the woman, keeping birth normal, recognising complications and getting urgent skilled help when required in a timely fashion. As the midwife protects the birthing space, the midwife facilitator/faculty protects the learning space, having a dual role of custodianship.

It is a privileged position to be a custodian, 'protector of', and we must hold this responsibility in high regard. The midwife has always had a revered role through time, mentioned in many sacred and ancient books. Considered one of the oldest professions, midwives assisted with birthing for rich and poor women including royal births until medical men – in advancing the articulation of management of birth through surgical means – discovered an earning potential.

Teaching too has seen a similar disconnect as the learning process was manipulated with the intention of increasing earnings. Students from time immemorial tended to learn in a close working relationship with a skilled person, a teaching and learning method known as apprenticeship. Modern educational methods were to see changes here too; with advancing articulation of teaching and learning, educational institutions saw the earning capacity in having large numbers of students in classrooms, 'bums on seats', which led to an erosion of the apprenticeship model. Worldwide we are struggling to return to teaching and learning methods that support the individual natural learning needs.

Two and a half thousand years ago a young boy, it seems, had obviously watched his mother as she practised the craft of midwifery, because he was later to align his teaching philosophy to that of being a 'midwife teacher' with the student.

What he most probably saw was a kind, firm woman encouraging, supporting and empowering a labouring woman to birth her baby in a way that supported her normal bodily function. His life efforts similarly focused on encouraging and empowering students to think for themselves and coined this method of teaching as the 'midwifery' teacher.

This young boy was to grow up to be our most famous philosopher of all time and has influenced every philosopher since then. As with so many enlightened and challenging thinkers he was imprisoned and killed for encouraging his young students to question the politics and customs of their time. His name was Socrates; he challenged traditional teaching methods of his time encouraging critical thinking and individual thought and development above the acquisition of material belongings.

His method is known today as the Socratic method of teaching. I have to remind you that this was over two and a half thousand years ago and still we are challenging teaching methods that are in complete disconnect with how individuals and groups learn; the normal bodily function of birthing is still being hijacked. In 2014 a world-renowned French birthing specialist Michele Odent insisted that midwives were the key to keeping birth normal and that without them, birth would continue to be a surgical event for every woman.

So you can see that my book has two aligned key messages, *be the custodian of normal birthing and teaching practices* while addressing the quality of midwifery teaching and midwifery care practices. The book represents my belief as to how midwifery should be taught and practised based on several decades of working with women and students and a passion for work-based learning.

Reviews of my initial draft of this book told me that they found the teaching /faculty terms confusing and requested some clarification. Having asked them what they understood by faculty, coach, supervisor, facilitator, teacher, tutor and mentor – the list is endless – they told me that these terms are interchangeable and that individually they mean different things in different countries and even in different hospitals and educational institutions in the UK. So my solution here is that whenever any of these terms are used they are basically a person who is supporting the learning of a student. Perhaps I should just use the term teacher since the title of my book is *Teach, Don't Tell* (*telling* is not *teaching*); it might possibly reduce the amount of confusion for the reader.

Now to share with you my view for the future of midwifery and midwifery teaching in the face of continued medicalisation and adherence to the traditional teaching methods. What is currently happening around the world to address the MDG is that the World Health Organisation (WHO), the International Confederation of Midwives (ICM) and many other NGOs, allocate funding to developing countries to meet the urgent need for more midwives as they are seen as one solution to advancing the status of women and reducing infant and maternal deaths. This is in contrast to doctors and legislators in both developed and developing countries, which still prevent midwives form working and learning.

Sadly and embarrassingly, even in my own birth country, Ireland, there is huge medical and legal opposition to how a midwife works. This is reflected in the cry: "*Ireland, no place for pregnant women*" by the Association for Improvement in Maternity Services Ireland, a voice for Irish pregnant women; you can find stories about the plight of Irish women at http://aimsireland.ie. I trained as a midwife in the UK, where there is strong support for the autonomy of the midwife with its own professional body, the Royal College of Midwives (RCM), and the Central Midwives Board overseeing standards that ensured that midwifery was recognised as separate from nursing, with its own philosophy of care that aligned with the word midwife as that of being *with woman*.

So you can see that much work needs to be done in both developing and developed countries and you are the key to help change all this. Teach the basics really well with skills as the most important facet; imagine what you could do to change this scenario. Curriculum design for midwifery programmes now sees midwifery skills as crucial. Unfortunately in the past initial midwifery programmes were theory focused which led to the dangerous situation of midwifery qualifications being awarded where very few midwifery skills were acquired. This was due to medics not allowing the student midwives to actually give world-recognised midwifery care as enshrined in the WHO definition of the midwife.

Moving forward from this situation, in one developing country a midwifery teaching team/faculty strive hard and with passion, having designed and managed a range of midwifery programmes including the country's first midwifery undergraduate degree on 'train the trainer' programmes. Ensuring the high quality of these programmes, this midwifery faculty team personally facilitated midwifery skills practice sessions in many corners of their country, bringing advanced training to nearly 500 midwives and midwifery teachers in the last five years.

Simultaneously this midwifery faculty team rebuilt their midwifery association directly in line with the MDGs. They epitomise the term 'Be the change you want to see', by being role models initiating little changes that led to great beginnings.

I currently have the privilege of working with this faculty team and am amazed at their dedication and perseverance, often putting in ten hours of work six days a week! I also had the privilege last year of visiting a midwife's birthing room set up in her own home in a remote village. She explained to me how she facilitated a mother giving birth to her baby on a draped mud floor; how privacy and dignity were protected and how she managed emergencies by being ready with everything that was needed including having arranged transport in case a transfer to hospital was needed. I came away with a real sense that here, in this mud room, the privilege of facilitating the women's transition to motherhood was truly enacted at a custodian level that no brightly lit, sterile clinical area can match.

Imagine how the birthing system of the woman's body is nurtured in this scenario. A particular obsession of mine when caring for a woman in labour, is to protect her birthing environment to allow for maximum influence of her limbic system.

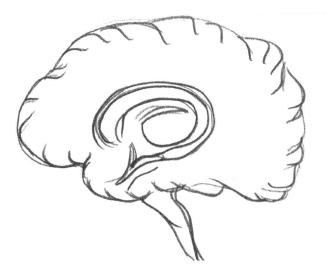

Very briefly, this is the part of her brain that supports her normal birthing function without her having to think too much about it, in the same way that her heart and lungs function just as designed; in fact, thinking about it could interfere with the natural process, as do bright lights, noise and strong smells. So I support the natural process, but am also skilled enough to notice when there is a deviation and to intervene or get help as appropriate. There is no room for complacency; safety must be paramount while supporting normal birthing mechanisms.

This links to how midwifery students learn to be skilled midwives. Learning does not have an exact defined limbic-type system that I have yet come across, but many theorists have said that humans have the capacity to learn in enabling environments, with the guidance of a facilitator. I see a parallel with the midwife being the custodian of the birthing space and midwife faculty too being the custodian of the learning space. In this protected learning space we can all learn together, mindful that the student is also a colleague alongside the qualified staff in the health care setting.

The privilege of being in this space is to understand the complicated lives that the people you come into contact with have, so being kind and empathetic, not in competition with each other, is what is wanted. It can be heart breaking to see women not supporting each other when we already have enough obstacles set against our potential for development. I was once told that the reason people are unkind to each other in certain situations – not sharing skills and knowledge and being rude – is because they don't want another person to be more knowledgeable or skilled than them, or even to have more of anything. There is some thinking that if you know as much as a colleague does they won't be needed and will lose their job, so the colleague is reluctant to share knowledge and skills. This is a sorry state when in actual fact at least a million more midwives need to be trained worldwide, so it must follow that we need thousands more midwifery teachers.

Chapter 2

Change attitudes and build skills and knowledge

Change attitudes? You must be wondering what I am on about. Think about the last chapter; what were the attitudes that would impede learning and practice? When officially training to be a teacher in the 1980s and 1990s I was taught that you should deliver knowledge first, skills' practice and then adopt a belief or attitude (KSA).

This method of teaching and learning was advocated by adult learning theorist Bloom as he described the cognitive, psychomotor and affective domains of learning. Much curricular design for educational programmes is guided by this method of adult education. I call this an *espoused* theory as defined by Schön in the 1970s; that is, a theory that the body of educational knowledge says we should use rather than what we actually do in practice – '*theory in use*'.

This really embodies the knowledge-to-theory gap and I challenge this particular espoused theory because I believe that we somehow must address attitudes first, as attitudes block or enhance learning. So I want to articulate a theory in use, in my belief – address attitudes, imbed the skills and then consolidate with the underpinning knowledge, in effect from KSA to ASK.

My life experience of teaching and challenging traditional teaching methods has led me to the point of view that we act first out of belief and then come to know what it is we are about. I have found it interesting to look at the values and beliefs of people that led them to a certain action. Questioning those beliefs and values then extrapolates what it is they do, and then you can ask them what knowledge these actions and beliefs are based on. The results most often point to a body of power that impales their beliefs and values on the section of the community they wish to control.

For now I want to focus on looking at people's attitudes. Attitudes block learning; coming from a 'certainty value system', they leave very little room for new ideas to be embraced. If you are trying to teach something new or different from these values this leads to a huge hurdle: how do you do it? The answer for me is simple: go back to the obvious, but maybe, just before this, try to find out why the particular values and beliefs are held and expressed by the group you are working with.

Don't challenge this head on; instead go back to the basic fundamental reasoning under discussion... it's about finding out what the mindset is and understanding where it has come from. Consider this: in a developing country health care is provided by paid hospital staff and learning is provided by educational institutions that accompany students into the workplace as practicum as they call it. When there is a request from the educational institutions for student development to be supported in the practicum by permanent staff, then a senior hospital director responds 'why should they be learning when they should be working?'. The essence here is that they are there to work not to learn; imagine what values and belief systems uphold this behaviour.

You can't change mindsets with a telling session followed by an action and expect the miracle of values adaptation. Much more thought needs to be given to the prejudice that blocks learning, we all have them and we need to face them.

A long time ago I was undertaking a small teaching programme and was shown two photos; one where a student was sitting upright at a desk with a book and one where a student lounged with feet up on the desk, his chair tilted on two legs and his book on his lap.

I was asked by the programme facilitator to make a judgment as to which student was more studious and learning effectively. You can think about this yourself for a few moments. Your judgment will be based on a belief and values system that you have engaged with in your life journey. It will be what you think; interestingly you may wish to ask yourself, what might help you to think differently from what currently comes to mind. When we explore our attitudes, we question our actions and the knowledge that has entrenched these beliefs. You can see that if you hold a particular view either way, one student could be excluded and the other perhaps unfairly welcomed. So for the purpose of exploring your own values, suspend your belief for bit and explore the possibility of thinking differently, perhaps even the opposite from what you might openly express.

We hold on to our attitudes because they give us a sense of surety, where we feel a sense of comfort. I once read a book titled *Feel the Fear and Do It Anyway* by Susan Jeffers and there are similar books in circulation today, and the crux of these books is that we should recognise that a lot of fears, beliefs and values are to a great extent designed to keep us in line with something or other.

We should question these beliefs and values and ask ourselves for whose benefit it is to behave in this way or uphold this belief. These beliefs are aligned to fear – if I don't behave in this way the consequences will be painful. At some level we need to reassess the risk. I'm not suggesting running across a busy road without looking – no one is encouraging you to 'play chicken' – but we need to look at what is imagined and what is real fear/danger. It's about having the discussion about values and beliefs. Who benefits? Who is in control? What relevance do these beliefs and values have to the particular skills and knowledge that need to be covered? When you continue with this train of thought you open up your mind to possibilities not just for your student but also for yourself.

Another book in a similar vein that I found inspirational is *Lean In* by Sheryl Sandberg, encouraging the individual to put oneself forward, instead of waiting to be invited or given permission. A core concept of this book is: 'if you were not afraid, what would you do?' and the response 'go do it', asking what you are afraid of, pushes you to question what it is you believe in. You will be surprised how some of these ideas seem to melt away, especially when you question who is benefitting from these beliefs that you hold. In considering this you may become aware that attitude change opens up room for new learning.

Recently, I had the privilege to teach the tutors of doctors and midwives in an international 'train the trainer' programme (TOT) on how to teach midwifery. Doctors and midwives have completely opposing belief systems about how birth should be managed, not to mention a whole belief system about their status in society. You know it is OK that they do have different care philosophies because midwives are what I call '*normologists*' and doctors concern themselves with *pathology*.

Pregnant and labouring mothers need midwives to be skilled normologists and doctors to be skilled at assisting when deviations from normal occur.

Midwives also need to know how to manage emergencies in the absence of a doctor. Interestingly with my initial week's work with this particular TOT, a participant doctor informed me that she was allowed to practice on real patients because permission was given by her senior but then went on to say that this privilege could not be afforded to midwives and they should practice on dummies, or simulators as they are called there.

Despite this clash of minds this was indeed a rare occasion for doctors and midwives to share the same discussion space in this developing country. The doctors learnt a lot about normal midwifery and how to restrain their surgical urge, while the midwives got to understand that the doctors often found themselves in a rush, which encourages surgical management of a normal physiological human event. While the power base and the social status base never left the room, an understanding of the precious capability of a human to grow and give birth naturally was shared by all and, luckily, I had the opportunity to facilitate the birthing of two babies with this group of midwifery trainers in the attached hospital without the need for surgical instruments. Actually managing the doctors' distress that kept their hands poised on scissors for the duration of the shift in the maternity ward was most challenging for me!

These TOT sessions began with attitude questioning; much skills practice followed and then the knowledge became evident in reality. So, there are attitudes about how people behave, how students learn. Let's look now a bit more closely about how students learn.

What type of learner do we have today? It is true to say we are in a changing world of learning and education, probably the biggest change since print. The Internet has unleashed the freedom for learners to independently seek knowledge for themselves; the need to move away from chalk and talk is more crucial now than ever. Our students can read, they can find information out for themselves. So what are the issues really and what is our role as teachers? The days of telling are finally over. Today's learners need help to question their beliefs and apply what they have been learning for themselves. Engaging with the changing world of internet use is what will benefit learners, working alongside learning technologists so that learning resources can be designed with the students' needs in mind. Students will come to the classroom having already questioned their own beliefs and values, and will have an idea of how they would like to advance their practice. This is called 'flipping the classroom' and together with the ideas of 'just in time teaching', education and training will be completely transformed as we all become more attuned to personal learning needs. We can choose how and when we want to do what: follow the many experts online through their blogs and social networking, and engage in discussions about real life experiences.

Imagine students videoing a skills session and then, during their tea break, replaying the video over and over again discussing skills points and what they have seen in practice. After leaving the skills classroom they go home and put the video on a social networking website to fellow colleagues thousands of miles away; the ripple effect is one where attitudes and skills are explored in depth across continents. The potential for a *theory in use* to become a globally accepted theory is so enterprising. I read somewhere a few years ago that the age of institutional education will come to an end as long as the explosion of online facilitated learning continues to expand. Students will seek out experts who have tailor-made programmes for them; it is an exciting time and teachers need to keep abreast of developments so as to be able to continue support and learning with the student.

Teachers cannot keep their students in cages any more, or 'bums on seats', with a fixed set of attitudes as to how their institution or current curriculum design attempts to control learning. We need to be brave and challenge the status quo of those in power who would like to keep things the way they are.

Chapter 3

Mobilise the learner

I want to share with you what is happening in the learning situation: see the student as they find a cage for themselves, a safe place where for some time they can become passive recipients of learning. You, on the other hand, find your place at the top of the class and for a while everyone finds comfort in their places. The student sits back and becomes passive as they wait for your instructions, at first hanging on your every word, and I can hear them silently asking you 'give me the knowledge'; you are prepared, or perhaps not, but the session begins with you talking at them and before you know it you are possibly both wondering what's the point of being there. The students shift around in their chosen cages, confined and comfortable as long as you don't ask them to think for themselves. You realise this is how traditional teaching has gone on for years despite most teachers having some induction in learning theories.

You may or may not have prepared a lesson plan and you know things should be different, but the classroom is set up in rows, the chairs even have little tables that actually slot the student in; it feels rigid, fixed, cemented. You want it to be different; you search in the back of your mind for a strategy that might work with this particular group; you scan each student for clues as to an appropriate method and somehow you realise that the students are actually asking you permission, by their expression, to engage more. Their eyes become more enquiring and you feel their thirst for knowledge but are perhaps frustrated that they are not interactive enough and that your teaching session somehow feels like very hard work.

At first the fidgeting in their cages is expressed through asking permission to go to the bathroom; some will just go, either way, after a while their cages become restrictive and they too want change, but they want it to be painless, 'don't push us too hard'. So you come up with an energiser that allows the student to leave their cage and maybe form a shoulder massage chain and shuffle clockwise around the room. The atmosphere becomes temporally electrifying, chatter and shuffle compete to be heard and after a few minutes the energiser stops and everyone resumes their positions, once again caged awaiting the theory download.

You continue with what you have planned to teach, engage the students in questioning and answering, but soon become frustrated by their lack of engagement as only a few keep responding; you ponder that some need not just permission but to be challenged too. You think about your role in caring for women on their journey to give birth and you remember how important it is for them to mobilise, to feel in some control – the normal process of the inevitable journey. So you make a firm decision that the students will not remain in their seats for the whole duration of the session. You tell them that they are allowed to move and that their particular seat does not specifically have their name on it, not even the particular spot in the room. You gain their cooperation to change the layout of the room which encourages movement.

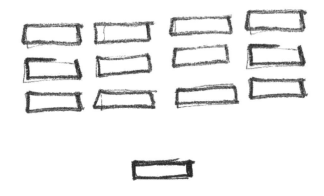

As they move the furniture around you notice some are apathetic while others welcome a sense of autonomy as they direct how the seats should be set; while they are doing this you talk to them about learning spaces and agree that how they are setting up the learning space will be an improvement. From this exercise you note that the apathetic learners will probably want their cages back and you will need to use all your imagination to actively engage them; they are not quite ready to take responsibility for their own learning and a huge burden bears down on your shoulders as you feel the weight of this responsibility. As the furniture is moved around the classroom, you resist attempts to shove the chairs and other furniture into an interactive format as you watch the clock ticking and think how much you have to get through.

Soon everyone is settled, a sense of calm returns and you engage with each student equally with the new layout as you notice more upright poises and attentive eyes, each able to see all their fellow students.

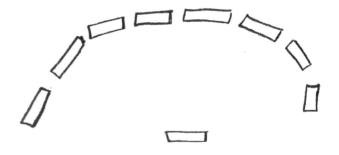

No learning environment will exactly fit the topic or skill that is to be learnt so a lot of improvisation will be needed; imaginative learning is required to make use of all the seen and unseen resources available. Use the table as a bed with a real participant to bring the topic to life. Manikins, or simulators as they are sometimes called, are useful, but to enhance the learning experiences of your student encourage their participation thus allowing communication skills to be taught and observed by the class. This enables dignity and respect to become a clear imperative and easily mobilises the students as they have to get out of their seats.

At first students will resist engaging in this type of learning for fear of making a fool of themselves or even for cultural reasons where discussing and demonstrating birthing positions can feel forbidden, but once they become engaged they enjoy the freedom of movement and expression. It very often leads to you having to cut the session short as you will run out of time. It is quite interesting to watch the dynamics of students once they have been mobilised out of their chairs; some take charge while others withdraw and are happy to be directed. It is at this point that you encourage the shy ones not to allow themselves to be bullied or submit to the ideas of the leading student; an opportunity for teaching teamwork presents itself and the students can learn from each other as they take turns in various roles of simulated learning.

You will also notice that some students will want to make their way back to their seats as they tire from having to think and engage as opposed to being recipients of learning in their seats. Patience is needed at this time and gentle coaxing to get them to return to the challenge of mobilised learning. Mostly this type of learning is noisy and appears chaotic at first but trust in the fact that learning will take place though it may not follow your lesson plan; focus on the key concepts you want the student to take away from the session and allow time for reflection and recap before concluding the learning.

The teacher, a desk and topic are only an educational experience; include everything available to you, for example, the fixed resources such as walls, doors, ceiling, and windows. Consider contextualising the space. Think about it… for example, you wouldn't want to teach a cooking class in a history room, unless it was a session on the history of cooking, so assess the potential for every available space being used to give the key messages for that session that you want the students to take away with them. Remove any items from the walls that are not relevant to your session leaving space for you or the students to put products of the learning from this session up on display.

More specifically the students themselves should be given authority to display their understanding of the concepts you are teaching on charts and then put them on the walls themselves. Don't worry about things not being perfect, or the odd spelling mistakes, sometimes we learn most by little errors as someone in the group will hopefully spot the error and it can be corrected allowing the whole group to learn.

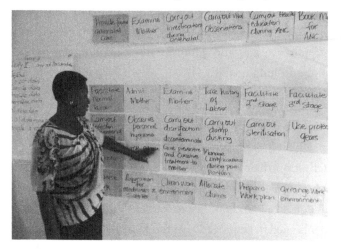

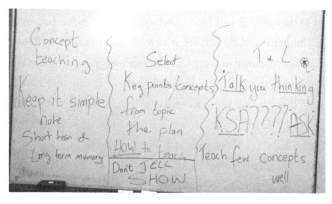

Imagine you are teaching in the clinical area – how would you mobilise the student in the workplace? Just like the classroom and clinical skills in classrooms, see the workplace as a learning environment that needs to be orientated to a culture of learning for all. Inform all management and ward staff in the work arena that when students are in the workplace they are there to learn. More specifically when you are with the students encourage all staff on shift to be interested and welcome in any learning event – including support workers and administrators in a non-threatening and non-judgmental way.

Also invite those on duty to comment and even share their wisdom and this creates an atmosphere of respect while also giving opportunities for permanent qualified staff to reflect on their own knowledge and skills. Mobilising the learner in their workplace includes encouraging them to ask questions and not just to loiter in the background. Students need to be proactive in their learning and not depend on a member of staff to offer to teach them something; in reality this is not likely to happen as in some hospitals permanent staff do not see it as their role to teach students, they see teaching as the role of the faculty member from the university that accompanies the student. Contextualise the workplace by having wall charts in places that are frequented by students so they can recap key important points, for example in the treatment and dirty utility rooms, even the linen cupboard. In rest/staff rooms have notice boards that focus on what particular groups are studying at that moment in time and remember to change them frequently; better still get the students to take charge of some of these displays so they can put up what they are working on.

Mobilising the learner takes them out of their passive role to an active role where they take responsibility for their own learning. Any movement in the classroom/learning setting awakens the student and this can be seen when energisers are used. So getting the student more active is really an extension of the energiser towards active learning and learning by doing. Why is mobilising the learner so important to me? It is about giving power back to the learner to be more involved in their own learning and to realise that teaching in controlled, rigid learning situations often leads to false and inadequate outcomes. My philosophy of midwifery, that of being 'with the woman', also inspires me and my teaching philosophy; being with the student.

To a great extent I mirror my care of women with my facilitation of students' learning. In midwifery care it is important to mobilise the parturient woman to allow for natural physiology to take place; similarly with the student, mobilising them allows for learning to flow much more easily and efficiently as the student is using all of their faculties, including hearing, seeing, feeling, and sometimes even smelling and tasting. This is referred to as tactile learning and is associated with a better grasp of the concepts being taught with the added benefit of information entering the permanent memory compartment of the brain.

Chapter 4

Show, involve, allow

This chapter is really about encouraging you to show your students 'how' and some of what I have to share with you may be a little repetitious but will be from a different slant and I hope you will absorb the most important messages.

Consider your prominent style in teaching; it is probably researching what you need to teach, making notes of some sort and delivering your notes by lecture or PowerPoint. This is really just telling and telling by itself is not teaching; there is an old adage: 'tell me and I will forget, show me and I may remember, involve me and I will never forget'.

So in paying attention to these wise words ask yourself why teachers focus so much on just telling. A very important development in today's students is that they can find their own sources of being *'told'* – remember, they can read! They can ask their colleagues, and follow informative blogs online. Today's students actually know more than their teacher in some cases because they have done extensive reading around the subject they are interested in. So where does that leave teachers today?

Teachers must move from telling to showing and involving students in learning. How do you do that? Well first of all you have to think about where the students have to apply their learning? What is their learning for? It certainly is not just to know! So you have to find strategies to bring the topic you are teaching to life. Improvise with the learning aids that will help to show the students what you mean when you are explaining a concept.

Choose your learning aids carefully; this is where a lesson plan is useful, because it means you have to give your resources a considerable amount of thought. You cannot just hope it works out, use your understanding of how students learn to help you plan a session that is effective within the given set time, space and resources. Personally I have learnt to trust my own resources as I have found on many occasions that resources provided are wholly inadequate; in some cases even where resources are in abundance they are locked away, and forbidden to be used for fear of them being damaged.

My colleague, while working in a developing country, discovered a room full of donated learning aids and was excited to take out a certain suturing teaching aid but was told that on no account must it be removed from the storage room as it would get damaged; instead she discovered that the locals used a pot scrubbing pad which actually quite effectively supported the demonstration and practice of basic suturing methods. The learning aid that was locked away in a storeroom was similar to a manikin/simulator and would have given a more realistic experience of having to place sutures in tight spaces. I generally like to have my own resources with me if I can.

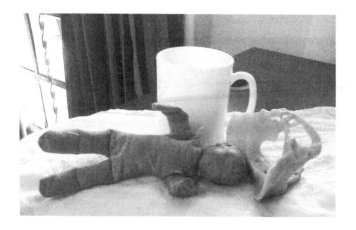

I once took out a small doll and pelvis to an African coun-try while on a midwifery consultancy project; it was called a pocket doll and pelvis and was to be the most valuable learning aid I have had, allowing hours of practice and discussion to evolve in learning situations. However, on another trip in a different developing country, I did not have my own resource with me and requested dolls and pelvises to be made available only to discover that when I was teaching and needed these items, the newborn dolls did not fit through the pelvis. I immediately had to im-provise and chose the smallest student in the session to pretend to be the baby, getting her to adopt a foetal posi-tion on the bed, draping a sheet over her shoulders by way of demonstrating the pelvis and then the student was in-structed to demonstrate with her own body how the baby moved through the pelvis during birthing.

It definitely engaged all the students, something which they will never forget and yet again skills of improvisation come to the fore. Not only that, think about the value of using scenarios as real as possible within your simulated teaching and learning sessions. If using a manikin make sure you place a fellow student or colleague with the manikin/simulator as an actor so the learning involves development of communication skills; actively involve and allow students to play out situations so they can master the communication skills that are needed in health care settings.

Tuning in to your students' learning needs and styles is crucial for real learning to take place. I will stay with this newborn check a bit longer to show you how to involve the students more. You noticed above that I asked the students to demonstrate back to me, thus allowing them to do or be involved, and this must make up the majority of any of your lesson plans. It is a quick way too of checking whether the students actually understand what you mean for action in the real world. Allow them to make mistakes and ask yourself why this miscommunication occurred – is it something you did not show adequately or is it a gap in the students' knowledge or even something they cannot grasp at the moment? A simple symbol of a happy, sad or OK face beside each of the students' name will aid a quick evaluation of who needs extra support; so put the happy-faced students with the ones who performed poorly so they learn from each other, and the competent ones learn how to teach.

When it comes to active learning – show, involve, allow – you don't have to do all the work yourself; being prepared with a lesson plan and visual aids is a good idea but when it comes to setting up the equipment and the room layout, get the students involved in this. I found that getting the students to set up simulators, contextualise the room and arrange the seating, gets them familiar with handling the resources and thinking about how they learn; they are more likely to move from the chairs to become involved themselves if they have been included in the preparations. It is interesting to watch how they take pride in how things are assembled, something that we, as teachers, sometimes give little thought to.

Now what about involving them in learning in the practice areas that I like to call the workplace? This is the most important place that we want them to perform competently, but remember we have the added challenge of ensuring the safety of patients and students. Real practical experiences are much more unpredictable and so too is the potential for learning. However, you have to trust that this is where most of the learning actually occurs.

With this in mind, see the workplace as a learning environment where you show, involve and allow students to engage. This requires you to have a good level of up-to-date skills yourself so you can care for clients and the health care environment at a level where the student participates while you closely supervise and support them. Permission, dignity and respect for the parturient woman are paramount; indeed you have not only to tune into your students' learning needs and styles but also the maternity client's health needs and wishes too.

Communication skills should be clearly demonstrated and you must be a role model in this sense no matter how frustrated you may feel on the day. Your students, client/patient and permanent staff are watching everything you do and say, looking to you for examples of exemplary care and instruction. Novice students should only touch a patient with your guided hand, so they learn when they need to be gentle and when firm.

As the students gain experience you should get a feel for their readiness to be more actively involved, get their ideas, allow them to plan care for a real or a simulated session, get them to script plans on the spot, keeping it simple with the key important concepts rather than a whole load of 'theory downloading'.

Rough + Simple + Quick Lesson Plan

Time	Concept Skill	What teacher will DO	What Learner will DO	Resources	Assessment
10min Chunks	Key concepts or skill not whole chapter or book!	facilitate. know your Student's needs. build on their Knowledge and skills	engage share apply co-teach Question	varied useful working allows practice	after each 10min Chunk. 😊 or 😐 or ☹

They can carry out their plans themselves, while you continue to supervise and give support – in other words hover. One thing you need to remember about learning is that it is a road to improvement, so don't expect the student to grasp all the concepts at one go and achieve a level of expertise rapidly; it is not going to happen. This means that you have to allow the student to fail in learning situations (not with a real patient of course and don't allow bad practice to be repeated over and over again!).

So, failing in a safe environment is key to allowing learning to evolve. Much has been written about the theories of how concepts are learnt, for example trial and error and repetition with reflection. Remember, you are there to facilitate learning so you need to have a good grasp of these theories and apply them, not expect them to know and understand concepts just because you told them. Telling is not teaching! Students will not understand, just because you told them and even if they rote learn it and are able to repeat back to you your words verbatim. It will challenge you to think about ways to show, involve and allow your students to participate and have some ownership of their learning. It is important to continually be with your student when they are learning so that their practice is supervised and monitored for their own safety and that of their colleagues and patients.

Making mistakes and misinterpretations are part of this learning because the student is trying to grasp a new concept in practice that might be difficult because of their own beliefs and values and quite often due to a lack of basic underpinning knowledge. This makes your role even more difficult as you patiently facilitate, watch, assess and improvise to enable the student to see, understand and replicate your intended teaching and learning becomes clear. This involves you paying close attention to the student's verbal and, most importantly, body language; you need to look for signs that they are struggling so much they are mentally shutting down. They will avert their eyes from you, bend their head and sometimes you see them adopt an almost closed position as they try to protect their own integrity and self-esteem. This is equivalent to them leaving the room, their learning situation and their belief that they can ever understand.

So while you may be comfortable with allowing your student to fail, you need also to reassure them that it is OK to make a mistake in the learning situation. Show them how trial and error, repetition and reflection, enable gradual and sustained learning. There is an old adage, which says 'practice makes perfect' so the focus should be keep doing and improving and not expecting the student to know and expertly do after one demonstration.

Chapter 5

Talk your thinking to the student

If 'practice makes perfect' what helps the understanding of that practice? How can your student know the thought processes that are going on in your head as you demonstrate a skill? This is about practice knowledge which differs from book knowledge as the knowledge is done in activities in the classroom and the practice settings. This is also known as tacit and non-codified knowledge (that is knowledge that can only become evident in practice).

Keeping in mind your intended teaching and pay particular attention to how basic concepts unfold in the learning situation. It is important to understand here that students can read text but cannot read your mind. Your skilful knowledge is unobservable and undecipherable unless you articulate your thoughts as you carry out activities. Codified and non-tacit knowledge is really the stuff of books that students can read for themselves, so if you waste a lot of your teaching session with densely scripted PowerPoint presentations and writing text on the whiteboard or black board you are really just theory dumping and missing the opportunity for teaching application learning.

Confused? Book knowledge is codified and non-tacit, doing knowledge is non-codified and tacit. Application learning is where tacit learning begins and also where learning is more likely to become permanent, rather than 'in one ear and out the other' as in lecture-led learning.

When you are demonstrating a skill, what thoughts come into your head? You are doing an activity and you want to share this tacit/non-codified knowledge and experience with your students. Think your thoughts out loud. This is indeed a difficult thing to do as tacit knowledge and non-codified knowledge is the stuff of intuition. Intuitive knowledge is a type of knowledge that is difficult to articulate, which is why it is not described in books and is therefore non-codified.

Intuitive action is where we 'do' without having to think too much about it, almost in 'automatic pilot' mode. The only way to bring this knowledge to the fore is if you talk through your thinking that guides your actions as you are doing an activity. Break down the steps, even if it doesn't make sense at first. Another thing I want to share with you is the controversy of knowing and doing knowledge. The doing of knowledge has unfortunately been accorded less importance, whereas knowing (academic) knowledge seems to have a more creditable reputation over doing knowledge.

Doing – which can be considered work – is seen as the remit of lower classes, while knowing is within the domain of the upper classes and they call themselves academics or scholars. It is important to understand this dilemma because the divide of doing and knowing knowledge is clearly responsible for the 'theory/practice gap'. That is the gap between knowing and doing. Knowers are given a special place in society, which personally I believe is unfair. It creates an imbalance in power, disgracefully belittling the worker (doer). This is how universities have managed to keep the power and technical colleges were seen as less worthy in terms of respect and reverence.

Dewey claims that ecclesiastical institutions had something to do with this division of knowledge and skills leading to the much-discussed theory/practice gap as knowers cannot articulate how to do and doers cannot articulate the knowledge that is the background to their actions. In some cases, where a sense of privilege is attached, there is a hold on knowledge and skills sharing as there is reluctance in some circles to actually reveal how to do and what is known.

I have found it very interesting in my travels to come across many people who gleefully tell me that they have done this or that degree in something and claim then to be an expert in that area merely because they have a certificate. On further enquiry I discover that they have never actually put into practice the theory they have learnt; on the other hand I have observed many skilful persons who carry out their duties with such diligence and skill without the need of a certificate. In some cases these skilful people do not attribute any value to themselves because they may not have a 'cert' to show for their efforts.

So how can this imbalance be addressed? Well I believe once we articulate our thinking more we will allow for practice knowledge to become codified and in that way gain more merit; this will be to the benefit of the learner who is struggling to master an activity, which seems almost unattainable to them. Until we do this, the educational institutions will continue to be the seats of power over real-world learning and actions. It means that the university and the workplace have to be more 'joined-up'.

During my masters studies in work-based learning, I co-designed an undergraduate degree that necessitated the university lecturers going into the workplace with the students to support the application of learning. I discovered that university lecturers were reluctant to frequent the workplace feeling more comfortable staying in the university grounds; perhaps they viewed it as beneath them to be present in the workplace. However, when they did venture into the workplace both they and workplace employees benefitted from the interaction. University lecturers became more workplace aware and the workplace employees had access to academic thinking. An interesting old adage is that if you are in a discipline and are not very skilled, teach – the phrase 'if you can't do, teach'! It is also true to say that some very skilful persons cannot teach, partly because they are unable to articulate what they are doing in reference to evidence-based practice but also through lack of understanding and appreciation of learning theories.

I have worked with many skilful colleagues who loathe having students and see them as an impediment to their daily work whereas others welcome students and see it as an opportunity to keep themselves and their workplace colleagues up to date and innovative. Firm ties need to be established with universities and practice areas; this is probably better managed within international universities that ensure a university-paid teacher (faculty) accompanies the student to the practice area and remains with them throughout their shift. The problem with this is, if the teacher is following an outdated curriculum, the student and the practice area staff are stifled, which leads to the persistence of a medical model of care. International universities are reviewing their midwifery curricula in an effort to address the MDGs.

I have been working with two African universities and a School of Nursing and Midwifery specifically looking at how midwifery is taught, insisting on a more practice-based and dignified approach to the care of women, babies and students. Imagine during a collaborative scoping exercise to identify what an African midwife does: the team were required to break the midwife's role into tasks; I offered the alternative approach instead of considering that the midwife undertakes units of care, not tasks, when looking after the mother and baby. This met with a lot of resistance but eventually was adopted when all could see that it implied a dignified approach to care. When it came to the role of the midwife in the labour room the group collectively insisted that the midwife managed labour; this was something I had to challenge. I stood up and said, 'midwives are custodians of normal birth; we facilitate birth and manage emergencies'. It took three days of me persisting with this and continually reminding the group of the definition of the midwife before it was adopted.

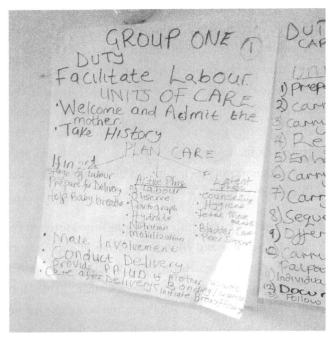

Curriculum development is crucial as teachers themselves can be stifled. I observed a midwifery teacher examining a pelvis with a student; the student was able to name every point on the pelvis verbatim like reciting the times tables. I considered that very little of what the student had just recited would help her facilitate normal birth; personally I prefer to teach the physiology of the pelvis, what it actually does and how it functions during pregnancy and labour. I asked the teacher why the student was not visualising the pelvis as an amazing adaptive structure, and she replied that is was down to the curriculum and the assessment strategy. The important thing to take from this discussion is that there is a theory/practice gap and one way this can be addressed is by 'talking your thinking' to your student so that the knowing and the doing meet whenever you are working with a student.

Let's focus on on-the-job training, which is where people really learn how to do. Foster a way for the student to learn from the everyday happenings in the workplace; see the workplace as a key learning environment where everybody learns, not just the student. It is easier to talk your thinking in the practice setting and to include all the elements of the real world that would not be present in the classroom.

Consider: real patients, the health care environment, visitors, other members of staff, managers and equipment all impact on the real world and that can never quite be replicated in the classroom. In the workplace learning opportunities are numerous, often unplanned, so thinking on your feet is required and if you talk your thinking on your feet to the student, they will begin to pick up tacit knowledge. This is also a way to show the student how to think critically, develop their reasoning and decision making skills as they observe you thinking and doing rather than just doing with no articulation or interpretation of your actions. The student will get the opportunity to see how, at times, you doubt that your actions are appropriate and listen as you critically analyse what is best to do, with reference to evidence-based practice, your own experiential knowledge and also reference to current workplace policies and procedural guidelines.

An example of this is when a skilful midwife examines a pregnant woman's abdomen; a student may watch as the midwife's hands navigate the woman's abdomen in a sequential order. To a novice it appears as if the abdomen is just being prodded and has missed that, in the 30 seconds prior to the palpation, the midwife has made mental notes about the mother and baby's state of health purely by looking and regarding the woman's abdomen. This information is absorbed into the midwife's decision-making brain and leads her to continue her examination which may then include a further examination to add to her findings regarding the abdomen.

What will the student have learned purely by just observing these actions? Generally we do not learn by loitering; there was a custom in healthcare education based on 'see two or three then get on and have a go'. This is changing now with the availability of simulators and online learning. There are video replays of practices where the practitioner is talking their thinking and then the student can practice on a simulator followed later by supervised practice in a real health care setting. Doctors, it seems, are better at talking their thinking as the student doctor's learning needs appear to take precedence over the patient. Midwives and nurses prioritise the patient's care needs over their learning needs. This is an interesting observation; you will see many doctors on what could be viewed as learning rounds for the medical students with the patient seen as a case study to this end.

I have found in practice that quietly talking my thinking and my findings helps the student and the mother to understand what is happening, allows for questions to be answered, doubts to be articulated and decisions to be made or changed based on subsequent findings.

The art and science of midwifery is displayed and a reminder that there is no surety; findings and decisions are only as good as the experience of the person undertaking the particular assessment. So how do we make visible the invisible? Remember, the students cannot read your mind, but they can hear you articulate your thoughts and match them to your actions, putting theory and practice together.

I have mentioned in the book how much learning can be drawn from a simple handshake; it happens so briefly and goes completely unnoticed by the students, yet to linger on this simple social interaction opens up a huge amount of learning for the students – communication skills, dignity and respect for the patient, the patient's state of health including social health.

It is true that talking your thinking lengthens the time of the interaction when you may be in a hurry. It is not necessary for every activity that you carry out; it may be that you get the student to talk their thinking to you and this enables you to assess their practical knowledge. It never ceases to amaze me how surprised colleagues and students are merely with the articulation of the thinking during a handshake. A skilled health care worker collates a mass of mental notes when shaking the hand of their patient/client or relative. Interestingly there is not a tick box in the patient's notes to document this information in the same way you would document a temperature or blood pressure. This is to do with codified and non-codified knowledge as discussed earlier. I wonder if you can decide if it is tacit or non-tacit knowledge.

We should be descriptively writing these findings in the notes; instead they stay in the minds of the health care person who has undertaken this assessment, which is a shame because it is valuable information revealing the social, emotional and physical health of the woman. If, the health care worker/teacher, talks their thinking to the student and then write a detailed account of this thinking in the patient's notes; this knowledge will then become codified and give credence to doing knowledge. So for the sake of the student you must articulate your thinking then encourage them as they are gaining confidence to articulate their thinking back to you. It will become second nature (intuitive) to them, will allow their doubts a voice, encouraging them to search more for clues to make judgments and decisions as to the best care for the patient and their learning.

Chapter 6

Advocate for real learning experiences

Assertiveness can be difficult in most societies; it begins with a confidence in your knowledge and experience and a belief in how students should be supported with real learning experiences. Be confident in yourself and foster confidence in your student. I often align these values with how you would instil belief in a woman that her body is designed to give birth; so too is the student capable of learning skills and performing them well in the right environment.

OK, can I share with you about being confident and believing in yourself? I have practised a lot on this particular issue and it comes down to the right body poise, which might seem ridiculous but feeling good about yourself is an art form; you have to consider the mountain that you must climb which includes a dose of making you feel you are credible and will not be thwarted. Forces are set against you and you will need a list of supporting buffers to protect yourself. I cannot insist more strongly how you must believe in yourself and not be put off from you path by ill-wishers which is exactly what they are and when you see them in this light you are empowered to believe in your mission. Walking with purpose is said to increase the self-belief hormones that propel you to your goal. Use this to help you be confident. Exercise regularly so that your muscles are strong and hold you strong. Breathing is very important here if I haven't shared this with you earlier; I want to stress the importance for you to learn how to 'belly breathe', a breathing rhythm I teach parturient women to enable them to have enough air needed to sustain brain and muscle function. The same is true of any unit of care we have to carry out; air is the purpose of breathing in carrying out the unit of care with confidence and belief in ourselves. Your students also need to learn how to respond assertively.

Just for clarification, I have talked about the apprenticeship model of midwifery training, which is predominantly used in the UK where the midwife student (apprentice) is teamed up with qualified practitioner (mentor) who teaches them the craft of midwifery; in many other countries in the world an American model of midwifery training is in place where the midwifery student does not have a mentor but is accompanied to the practice area by a university teacher (faculty).

I can remember an occasion in 2008 in a London teaching hospital where a midwifery student was in tears because of what her midwifery mentor had said to her. First I told the mentor that their student couldn't respond accurately to them because they were shouting and students don't learn when overly and unnecessarily stressed. I then took the student aside and advised her to articulate to the mentor midwife how her comments had made her feel; the result was that the student midwife learnt how to be somewhat assertive while also understanding the stress that the mentor midwife was under because it was her professional registration at stake, as she could lose her licence to practise if a student she is teaching makes a mistake. Empathy was required on both sides.

Recently when teaching midwifery teachers overseas I accompanied the teachers into the hospital to observe their teaching practice. Before doing so I advised them to try to not pass their stress on to the student. Midwifery and teaching can be very stressful and we have to find coping and adaptive strategies. You should be aware that there are many resources that you can use to help you feel a sense of confidence and cope with stress. You must first have the knowledge and experience to build up your self-confidence; for example, an iPod session on self-hypnosis can do this as does listening to any religious recital that you are familiar with. Whatever works for you, plan it in and give yourself the boost you need. Find a chant that you can say to yourself when you know you have to stand up for your beliefs and values.

I am proud to be a midwife
I believe in "being with" women and students

You will come across many situations where you are challenged and belittled; experience in both my personal and professional life has taught me that when you challenge an injustice the response may be one which belittles you. I say to you, stick to your conviction and enjoy the feeling of not taking the response personally; it is difficult to do but try it – act, decide and then let go. Another person's criticism is just that, their criticism; thank them and do not let go of your own passion. Detached assertiveness is what you need to develop both for you and your student. Challenge injustice at every turn; you are knowledgeable and skilful, you know how things should be, so say so with conviction. Show your student how to maintain eye contact and be strong in their belief of their knowledge and skill.

Recently I was supporting midwifery teachers in how to care for women respectfully in maternity care and appreciate the amazing power of women to birth their babies. On one particular afternoon in a government hospital while supporting the labour process of a first-time mother and demonstrating care to 20 midwifery tutors and eight hovering medical doctors, I was shouted at for providing a normal room and bed space for a normal labouring woman – why wasn't the woman in lithotomy?

Let me be clear: there are instances when this method of care is needed if deviations from normal progress are identified; but not from the outset with complete disregard for normal bodily function. I was confident enough to look this person straight in the eye and tell them that this was a midwife delivery and surgical equipment was not needed at that moment in time; and if it were I would gladly defer to her excellent surgical skills.

The important thing to remember is that women need mid-wives and sometimes women and midwives need doctors too. As midwives become more articulate in their knowledge and skills they will be able to hold a dialogue with doctors on a scientific level that will give them credibility. An example of this was when a degree student midwife shared with me that she was able to hold a dialogue with a doctor about how a newborn took its first breath and the discussion continued for some time, whereas beforehand her input might have been ignored and dismissed. This student sent me a photo of her with a baby on a resuscitaire, which would not previously have been allowed as midwives were often belittled, facing claims they did not have much knowledge nor any skills.

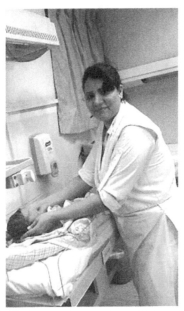

So focusing on assertiveness and advocating for real learning experiences I want to share the importance of role play when it comes to developing assertiveness skills, particularly when working in multidisciplinary environments. The classroom is as good a place as any to start with this; role playing managing an emergency where participants have to observe, judge, diagnose, delegate and assist at fast pace with clear diction and body language. The fish bowl or inner- and outer-circle technique can be useful to analyse the interactions between the participants and highlight those needing extra help and needing more practice in the classroom, before attempting this new skill in the workplace.

Of course this does need to be followed up in the workplace where you can support both yourself and the student by beginning conversations with those members of staff that you or the student would not normally talk to, for example a senior member or one from another discipline. I once remember a group of 18-year-old education students wanted to interview a head teacher for their project but were really scared of the head teacher and felt that they would be unable to speak to her. I brought the students into my office and they phoned the head teacher and began their conversation; when I observed that they were beginning to struggle I asked to speak to the head teacher and explained that these students were undertaking a project and that today I was focussing on helping them with their assertiveness skills. They then continued their conversations with her and found their voice and confidence. This was a facilitated real life learning experience out of the classroom and into the workplace.

Sometimes I think it might be an idea to have notices around qualified staff areas saying 'learner at work' just as you would have a 'men at work' notice, so that the student can have a protected space to transfer the new knowledge and skill to real experiences. In a way this facilitates safety for the student, yourself and the patient. It is really a form of supervision and mentorship. In creating this safe learning and practice space, be aware not to leave your learners unsupervised. As they are developing their assertiveness skills while practising their knowledge they may cross boundaries, get carried away and cause havoc in the workplace. I learned this valuable lesson while supporting practice-poor midwifery teachers in delivering a baby midwifery style; I instructed the co-delivering midwifery tutor to complete the hospital required documentation and return immediately to the skills classroom.

Back in the skills classroom I discovered that they had not done exactly as I had instructed but had interrupted a doctor beginning an episiotomy at which point the doctor left the room telling them to get on with it; they delivered the baby but did not repair the small cut the doctor had begun, instead instructing an attendant to tell the doctor to do the repair. Unfortunately the woman waited a while for the repair to be done, which was completely unacceptable. The midwifery teachers were severely reprimanded by me and the programme organiser. So, never leave learners unattended even if the learners are themselves midwifery teachers; learners can get carried away with any new skill they are developing.

Another sensitive topic that I want to share with you is how to teach progress of labour by undertaking additional examinations. In Britain, because the midwives facilitate the birthing of all normal births, British student midwives therefore get ample opportunity to learn how to facilitate normal birth and manage and assist with complications. However, in developing countries, this is just not the case because midwives in main hospitals are not allowed to touch labouring women and usually have to wait till they go to very rural places to develop this important skill. Before I go further it is important to point out that midwives should be just as competent at judging the progress of labour from feeling (palpating) the descent of the baby into and through the woman's pelvis per abdomen – that is just by feeling her tummy – just as they need to do when undertaking an internal examination.

How do you teach this skill? For the student it can cause issues of deep emotional consequence and you need to consider that the participants may have had experiences in their lives that may come to the surface at this time. Having paid attention to these important issues I found it helpful to use visualisation, by encouraging the participants to see, feel and imagine to find out relevant information as to the progress of labour. The particulars of the technique can be read in any textbook but bringing it to life enables the participant to mentally prepare themselves for actually doing the technique when the appropriate opportunity arises for them in the health care setting; it is a skill for the facilitator to seriously consider. In the workplace, be an advocate for real learning experiences, challenge injustices and don't let yourself, your student or the patient be taken advantage. Once you have accepted this challenge adopt a detached assertiveness approach – act, decide, then let go. Another person's criticism is just that.

Chapter 7

Talk with the theorists

I have shared with you the importance of having a good understanding about the theories of learning. This requires you to study the ideas of a variety of theorists old and new. Very often you study them in such depth that you get a feel for who they are. I once had a dinner conversation with an educational psychologist in London who shared her knowledge of Maslow. The experience for me was as if he were at the table with us and so I often say to students that when they find a theorist that they feel tuned to they should study them in detail by reading their life history and how they applied their theories in real life. Personally, having studied learning theories for thirty-five years and continuing to do so, I have decided that many development and educational theories are really built on old theories. When we think about the learners' needs, basic requirements must come first and cannot be ignored.

Maslow shares much about human basic needs and motivation. I do not intend this book to be an instructional book where you will find all the learning theories available. Merely I wish to share with you my story of how to teach and the influences along my journey of being so passionate about learning by doing and thinking. You will have to study the theorists in depth yourself to get the feel that you have shared a dinner conversation with them, allowing you to adopt or discard their ideas as relevant to you. You will not get to this point by just reading this book. So to begin your period of concentrated study, make sure that you are comfortable, fed, hydrated and with time scheduled where you will not be disturbed. These are basic needs for learning and I am sure you know the model I am referring to.

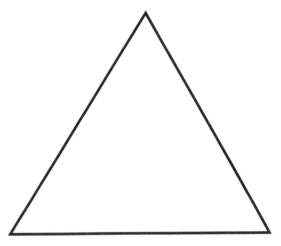

If not, this is a huge gap in your knowledge and you must attend to that gap immediately. Basically, the theory is about paying attention to the basic bodily functional needs of individuals. These basic needs are clearly obvious in many societies; for example, in some societies they welcome visitors by immediately offering them refreshments. From my own life experience in Ireland there was always a pot of tea brewing on the stove and visitors were always made welcome by tending to their basic needs of hydration and comfort so that they would feel relaxed and stay a while.

I mirror this philosophy with caring for parturient women and facilitating students' learning; as mentioned earlier, in the way that midwifery is being with the woman, as a facilitator you should be with the student. Ask yourself whether your students can learn by themselves, and who can help them? You may be curious to know that students don't actually need us as much as we think they do, or even as much as they think they do. Having read in depth learning theories from Piaget and Vygotsky I like to imagine having been invited to dinner where they are guests. I ponder on how the conversation would go, given their slightly different approaches to how people learn but also the similarities.

Piaget was adamant that children, if left alone, will learn by doing themselves; he shares his ideas on readiness to learn and devised a chronological framework of childhood development that is still used today.

On the other hand Vygotsky, 'the father of facilitation', shares his ideas on learning as evolving – similar to Piaget's ideas about learning by doing but with the added requirement of having a person next to them to guide and support the development to the next level.

Both see readiness to learn as important, but Vygotsky argues with Piaget that readiness to learn can be seen as below, within or above the comfort zone as far as the student is concerned; you can imagine that the dinner table discussion is quite vibrant.

Unfortunately Vygotsky died quite young and his theories were only found many years afterwards by which time Piaget's theories had become part of main stream education policy and practice; many of the learning theories both for children and adults have developed from early theoretical thinking.

Consider the adult learning theorists such as Kolb and Knowles and how the dinner table discussion would go. There would certainly be in-depth discussions about experiential and self-directed learning to-ing and fro-ing across the table. With the focus on adult learning the concept of reflection is brought to the table by Gibbs and Schön; this possibly differentiates children's learning from that of adults in that adults reflect and even plan whereas children forge ahead with their trial and error and repetitive doings. Children appear almost instantaneously to acquire concepts that lead them on to another explorative activity without fear or restriction. Adults have development impediments to their learning ranging from fear of failure to worrying that someone will think them stupid. This makes the facilitator's job difficult as they have to diagnose the impediments and get through to the learner and release them from their fears. Methods such as 'think, do and think again' nudge the learner into enquiry and active mode simultaneously, encouraging them to question everything with 'what' and 'how'.

Imagine the dinner is in full swing and Pablo Freire joins the table asking questions about education – for whom and by whom and for what purpose? His view of education is that it is procured for the powerful and delivered by followers to keep the status quo in place and you wonder if education empowers or suppresses learners.

Consider the content of learning sessions: whose ideas are we facilitating, what impact and benefit will particular sessions have? Freire's book *Pedagogy of the Oppressed*, considers the social aspects of learning, makes interesting reading. Freire shares his ideas about 'learning circles'. How people learn together and see what is going on around them rather than having a specific discipline designed by someone else dictated to them. Interestingly he talks about those who are oppressed becoming oppressors at the first opportunity which to me fits the bill of educational institutions that come down heavily on the teaching staff which is quickly displaced in good old Freudian style in the subsequent treatment of students.

Displacement theory was coined by Sigmund Freud to explain what is known by laymen as 'kick the dog syndrome' – something for you to look up if you are not familiar with this term. An old adage comes to mind here: 'it's nice to be important but it is also important to be nice'. The table is joined by modern-day learning ideas that include the availability and use of information technology with theories of 'flipping the classroom' and 'just-in-time teaching'. It could be said – and important to pay attention to the fact – that today's student learning facilitation needs have changed drastically. Today's students are very different from yesterday's learners in that they have access to, and choose to read and search for, knowledge for themselves. It makes sense then that the classroom/workplace should be a place to support and facilitate application of learning rather than insisting on theory dumping sessions.

In my imagination at the dinner table with the theorists, I can hear Piaget and Vygotsky mumbling in the background ssaying: "So, what's changed? We proved to you that learners can learn by themselves, they just need some help and support with application and progression to the next stage". The conversation becomes excitable as the presence of Socrates is expected. He arrives simply dressed and eager to share his passion in encouraging critical thinking; he reminds the group that his mother was a midwife and he fashioned his teaching methods on her *being with women*, encouraging, coaxing and empowering. Candles flicker on the table and a computer screen lights up the room – hard to imagine I know but try it, teach your student how to imagine, visualise and invent.

Information technology is going to completely change academic and skills-based learning. Over the past ten years a new discipline has entered the pedagogical (educational) field – 'learning technologist' has evolved, made up of computer practitioners and teaching practitioners who have grasped this monumental change. They work together designing classroom, workplace and online learning packages specifically for the students' new information technological learning needs. In class, learning resources will become more individualised or targeted to specific groups across disciplines. The table discussion declares that the future of teaching is predominantly online; 'super teachers' will facilitate students from around the world rather than being attached to one institution. Students will decide what and how they want to learn and as teachers or facilitators we must be ready for this change.

Learning is moving out of the classroom and is much more likely to take place in the workplace as lifelong learning becomes the norm. Excitingly, up-and-coming learning technologists for the Association of Learning Technologists (ALT) join us for dinner too and share a glimpse of how technology will further help individual and group learning.

Research is currently being undertaking to see how technology packages can help with the teaching and learning of tacit learning; that is really difficult to imagine but it is happening – see this website for more information https://www.alt.ac.uk/.

Early learning theorists focused on the learning and development of children because, at that time, adults were meant to be focusing on work. Now the concept of learning at work has opened up a whole new avenue for adults who see the potential to develop themselves; indeed this is demanded by our global evolving knowledge base. Boud, Garrick and Schön pipe-up and the concept of the 'learning milieu' is thrashed out at the table – the realisation that everything in the learning environment gains significance rather than just the teacher and student communications. Policies, procedures, social, cultural and political influences are brought to the table to the delight of Freire who nods in agreement. Learning at work embodies learning by doing and thinking; it has a discipline of its own known as the discipline of Work-Based Learning (WBL), a field that crosses all disciplines. You can be a teacher, midwife, manager, and you can advance your knowledge and skills in all areas through WBL by closely examining what you do at work, identifying how we learn in real situations.

The dinner comes to a close as a toast for 'educating for living' is called for by Socrates and his final words are *question everything* – imagine!

Chapter 8

Live the questions –
the uncertainty

In this chapter I want to share with you my passion for trusting in experience, trusting the learning situation you have involved yourself in and which, to some extent, you have manipulated for the maximum benefit of your student. In this sense you need to remember that lessons plans are only working documents; that they are a guide to help you focus on the key concepts you want to share with your students and the resources and strategies you will use.

So you have your lesson plan mapped out and you go to the learning situation, be it the classroom or the workplace. It just takes one change in the learning milieu (learning environment and everything that impacts on it) to alter everything and you find yourself improvising to fit the learning needs to the situation rather than sticking thoughtlessly to your planned script. It means letting go of the certainty and trusting the experience you find yourself in and your ability to improvise when needed. It is important to have key concepts that you want to facilitate for your student and to consider how the learning milieu allows for appropriate learning to take place. This will include human and non-human items, from administrative personnel to the curriculum document and the institutional space; a lot to

think about – awareness, appreciation and a relaxed con-
sideration of all these impacting elements.

A relaxed approach is needed to allow for any uncertainty
that gives room for your intuition to come to the surface
and space for the 'surprising' to happen both for yourself
and your students. This is not to say that you should go
unprepared; you should be prepared but not rigid. Do not
go through your lesson plan like a robot, or follow exactly
what you have been told to do without the 'teller' (manager) being present to be able to read the situation and adapt
as necessary. This includes managers and the following of
policies and procedures; remember they are guidelines and
best practice in ideal situations. Rarely are situations ideal
so some adjustments will need to be made even if you are
not sure what; you may need to listen to your gut instinct
as well as reasoning – a combination of both enables you to
read a situation and act accordingly. I have found myself in
many situations where I have had to completely veer from
my planned lesson or speech.

I remember being asked to speak at a conference and given
the topic for which I prepared only to find thirty minutes
before I had to speak that I needed to focus on a specific
area; even though the PowerPoint presentation had been
prepared, I managed to add a couple of slides and adjust
my speech 'on the hop'. On another occasion I was expected
to give a practical session to an audience and I was informed that about thirty participants might attend; in fact
nearly a hundred participants arrived. Can you imagine

the improvisation that took place for that to be successful? I had to completely rethink my script within five minutes and I resorted to getting a least ten of the participants involved copying my actions so that every participant could engage in the planned activity. I didn't think it would work but was completely going on my gut instinct, believing it might and it did.

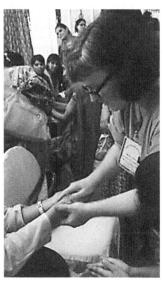

In a way I was living the uncertainty and trusting the experience. I remember one midwifery tutor once sharing with me a mantra of how to cope with uncertainty saying: "You may be new to a particular experience, but you are not new to the life". She meant that we can draw on previous experiences and adapt to the new one. Welcoming the uncertainty also allows you to expect the unexpected. I was once teaching a group of students about muscle function, focusing on the needs of the muscles to function optimally. This required the students to pay particular attention to muscle physiology. When they understood that muscles need a certain amount of magnesium to relax and calcium to contract it led them to understand how administering pharmaceutical magnesium can cause muscles to malfunction; for example, the effect on breathing that a large dose of magnesium has on the intercostal muscles that help with breathing. Therefore it is important to check for magnesium toxicity in the patient when on a magnesium infusion regime.

During another teaching session I asked the students to focus on the uterus purely as a muscle that had nutritional needs for it to function. Once the students worked through the physiology of muscle function, realising that muscles do not function when dehydrated or have an electrolyte imbalance, they could see that it was ridiculous to ask a labouring woman to be 'nil by mouth'. Giving birth requires the use of a major muscle (the uterus) and this muscle needs optimum nutrients and oxygen for sustained function over many hours.

Your session plan will to a great extent have learning outcomes as the end product of the learning experience, phrased: 'by the end of this session the learner will be able to understand, demonstrate or apply something or other'. This is codified knowledge, meaning book knowledge. Unfortunately this form of knowledge is gaining more credence to the detriment of non-codified knowledge, learning which must be acquired to achieve mastery but is nowhere to be found in text. It is the doing of the knowing, often by intuition and not outwardly visible to the learner. I like to use the handshake as an example to explain these phenomena. You will know that shaking hands in many cultures is a polite form of introduction and is indeed expected. So it is codified as an expected formal introduction which occurs in many situations; you may have heard a partially coded knowledge whereby if the hand shake is feeble this person is not to be trusted, but if it is firm and strong this person is genuine and sincere and can be trusted and even depended on.

Consider this further. A health professional greets a patient and shakes their hand; it all happens in the space of thirty seconds and the on-looking learner merely sees the respectful approach of the health care worker to the patient as it is written in the text – so codified knowledge in that it is evidenced and accepted as good practice. However the health care worker is amassing a lot of information about the patient in that handshake, which tells them about the patient's state of physical and social health – are they dehydrated, is there evidence of repetitive domestic toil or injuries to fingers or palm? None of this is evident to the learner because it is in the doing of care peculiar to a skilled health care worker and is not actually documented, thus not codified.

Non-codified learning is also known as tacit learning. So non-tacit learning is learning the art and craft of a discipline that cannot be learnt from books. Think about what's missing in textbooks and codified knowledge that actually prevents the learner from grasping the essence of a skill. For example, how does one learn how to ride a bike when there are so many individual skills that need to be learnt simultaneously to avoid falling off the bike?

As a facilitator you think about what particular instruction or facilitation of learning is missing that is preventing the learner from moving forward with their learning in acquiring a skill. I was recently teaching teachers how to expand on the knowledge about a patient's health just by focusing on the handshake and asking themselves what information they acquired during this act that gave them relevant information about the patient's state of social and physical health. As the demonstrations, reflections and discussions circled the room I discovered incidentally or intuitively that I could check the patient's pulse using my index finger while I was shaking their hand.

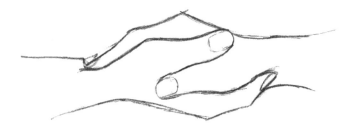

This is tactile knowledge, not visible but intuitive action, thus not obvious to the learner and indeed even the patient may not be aware. Non-codified and tacit knowledge has eluded science to a great extent because scientific facts have their own measuring tools that do not allow for tacit knowledge to be articulated as yet. Science focuses on what is measured by its own designed measuring tools. Dewey, an American educational philosopher, considers measuring with a ruler as limiting our further understanding of knowing length and depth from any other aspect.

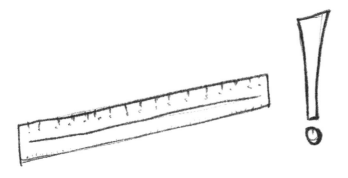

He also shares in his book that we are restricted by language, as there are times when no words correctly describe our experiences so we resort to similes and metaphors. He suggests that art and craft may allow us to depict tacit and non-codified knowledge but will depend on the knowledge and skill of the viewer or artist. It is an awakening concept to realise that the tools we use to understand our world are preventing us from knowing it further. Dewey thus writes in depth about man's 'quest for certainty', which has led to some absurdity in many instances – beautifully depicted in his book of the same title. He suggests we should live the questions and not constantly seek surety. This should give you some comfort in not always having all the answers and being honest about that. Also not expecting the learner to have all the answers either, or indeed understanding a situation fully. Trust in what you do know and feel is right, trusting the experience, rather than trying too hard to manipulate the situation to fit your rigid lesson plan and learning outcomes.

When we learn to live with uncertainty, we allow for unintended learning opportunities that may better fit the intended learning outcome.

Some thought is needed here as to why we search for certainty, why it is that we need measure using tools to be exact and then wonder why the desired outcome has not been reached. One measuring tool looks at one component of the whole; there is no measuring tool for the whole and the measure miscalculates the whole in focusing on one component. An example of this is when a midwife checking fundal height stops using her fingers and palms to estimate gestation age and health of the foetus and resorts to the current practice of using a measuring tape so it may be, so to speak, accurately documented.

Ask yourself exactly where the accuracy is. The midwife may comply with this new required measure but should still use her hand as the touch of the palm on the uterus tells us more than what can be measured. Also, if she fails to continue to do this, she loses the ability to measure the whole – intuitive feel about the wellbeing of the mother and the baby. We search for certainty out of the fear of the unknown, not realising our limited measuring tools are preventing us from actually exploring the unknown.

When we don't fully understand something we make up elaborate notions that somehow give us comfort and something to do. Perhaps even keeping and maintaining a status quo with a false sense of security. This is partially due to social/cultural control and Dewey describes in his book how some cultures design rituals that enable them to accept their unknown world, preventing them from actually understanding what is going on or taking steps to improve their situation. What comes to mind for me is dancing for rain rather than designing an irrigation system, pooling water and transferring it where it is needed. The world pipes oil so surely we can pipe water by now!

Dewey gives ample examples that show how cultures that have built up superstition around illness actually prevent the illness from being investigated – a 'head in the sand' approach. I want to relate this to how we teach students and expect them to learn. We have our curriculum, learning outcomes and assessment strategies – in a sense, prede-signed measuring tools. I am actually interested in what these tools are not measuring and how elaborate rituals are built around this when the students' actions don't exactly match these measurements. What comes to mind is students that don't achieve are failed and later we discover that they were actually dyslexic and were inappropriately supported. Dismissed, forgotten as the education institution finds strategies that supports its own measures.

I am sure you can think of many such rituals yourself. Perhaps one solution is to live with the question rather than making up an elaborate event/ritual that speedily surfaces and becomes embedded in practice. Question everything but don't expect all the answers; leave room for real solutions to evolve, allow learning to evolve.

Chapter 9

The novice to expert continuum

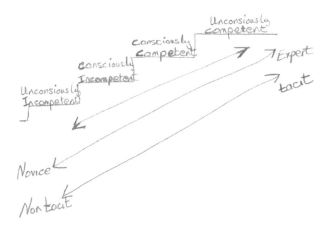

We are all always learners and the best place to be on this continuum is the consciously competent step but aiming for excellence in knowledge and expertise. I personally don't believe in perfection because as soon as we near a certain level of expertise (unconscious competence), evidence changes and we need to update. This is why lifelong and work-based learning is crucially important. We can never claim to know everything or behave in a way that implies we have superior knowledge. Very often our students and clients can be more widely read in some areas than we are so we should be ready to learn from each other. In this case we can perhaps see ourselves as unconsciously incompetent

97

in a constructively critical way; we don't know what we don't know, thus leaving room for awareness of this and rectifying it. We can reflect on and challenge our knowledge and skills every day and ask if we are up to date.

Keeping a journal or professional development portfolio is a good way to allow room for the recognition of the need for continuous learning. Most institutions and professional bodies expect practitioners and teachers to keep records of their continuing development. So if you haven't being doing this start immediately; record your thinking, new ideas and reflections regularly. If you attend an institutional update or read an article of interest to you write half a page on its relevance and applicability to you in the real world, or not, as you see appropriate. Keeping pictures and clippings of events you are involved in is also useful. Keeping up to date adds to your level of confidence as you emulate tacit learning, moving from consciously competent to unconsciously competent or expert, but don't allow yourself to become complacent because being at the pinnacle of expertise only lasts for as long as evidence and practice are current and you keep up to date and try out new ideas.

With today's mass of evolving knowledge and practice available online it can be difficult to decide what you should keep up to date with. An idea here is to make note of the questions that spring to mind and search for answers and direction in the literature. Remind yourself that we cannot know everything and this relieves you of the burden of trying to do exactly that. Don't be hard on yourself and don't promise that you can know and can do so much. When you have strong beliefs and values as to how something should be done, temporarily disagree with yourself and suspend your belief for a few moments to see what the possibilities and alternatives could be. There is never a single right or wrong way of doing something, only principles.

I want to share with you the concept of multiple 'ontologies' (knowledge that exists) here; it sounds like a strange word I know, but it is about recognising that each individual comes to a situation with a different view of the same topic/phenomena from another. Their beliefs and values can be so wide ranging that, for example, a psychologist, economist, medical doctor, nurse/midwife and pathologist will all view a simple blood test or report pro forma differently. When we view this multidisciplinary understanding and focus on a topic we learn from each other but also find a common vision. Latour, a French revolutionary theorist, refers to this as 'modes of existence'– in other words, each discipline exists within their own point of view that sometimes excludes other disciplines to the detriment of the care of the patient or training of the student. He suggests that we should disband current disciplinary demarcations and rebrand and find a common focus.

We sometimes expect that people should understand exactly where we are coming from in terms of our point of view. Why it is that we do not appreciate that people have different points of view is a mystery to me. Then I think that some communities build up a common belief so that generally there is a common understanding just for that particular group. However, as a teacher, if you cannot understand the students' point of view, how can you teach them? If you are going to just persist with what you have in mind, you lose the student in that process, the student is left behind. It can be almost impossible to understand every student's point of view but claiming to know and understand everything is a very dangerous position to be in. Even as a teacher it is OK to sometimes think I don't know what I don't know; we are all on continuous learning journeys and it is not true that if you don't know everything, or pretend to know everything, you will not be respected. We are learners always.

We reach a point of unconscious competence at a certain level but if we don't keep up to date with developments in our area we plummet to an unconsciously incompetent level very quickly where we can lose the respect of our students and colleagues because we insist that we know best and do not listen to what they have found out to be current knowledge.

Consider what it takes to learn something; I came across a minimum number of hours, a figure that may surprise you. No learning happens quickly, it takes time; and though modern teaching and learning strategies can to some extent augment learning, there is no getting away from the fact that learning takes time. The numerical figure I am referring to is one thousand hours. I need to ask you now if you are sure you know the difference between learning something and purely being able to repeat something verbatim. Be clear here, telling is not teaching and repeating is not knowing. Learning takes time; it is not instantaneous and reaches several levels at different times in the student's journey. When you have empathy for your own learning journey it helps to understand your learner.

In today's educational area, students sometimes have a grasp of knowledge and skill that we do not have ourselves as teachers and this is OK. This actually means they may have more knowledge and skill in some areas than we as teachers have ourselves. I have found that in just the one class or group you can have such a wide range of knowledge and abilities that you need to be very resourceful and attentive to develop all students but also watchful where students continue to think that they know more than they do.

Supervision and guidance while carrying out practical experience are very important. Internationally skills are learnt differently within educational and practice areas. For example, Australia, America and central Asia take the approach that disciplinary faculty employed by the university should accompany the learner into the workplace and support their practical experience there. In the UK an apprenticeship model is used whereby the learner is placed alongside a mentor in the workplace and the university link remains one of academic supervision and supporting the student and mentor.

There are advantages and disadvantages to these two different models. I find it a concern in countries that use a faculty model when the faculty member lacks practice skills themselves. It is hugely important that students have a good role model they can learn from, be it mentor or faculty. Those thousand hours include supervision and support in the workplace.

What I wanted to share with you here is the relevance to the thousand hours needed to master knowledge and skills. Generally in official learning programmes we have learning outcomes and descriptors to guide us teachers as we navigate the learner through their journey. Learning descriptors are useful as they help to navigate the student from one level of competence to the next level on a gradient of novice to expert. When you get a good grasp of this learning journey as a process you realise that it takes time to learn something and develop advanced skill. Learning outcomes guide you to support, supervise and assess the student's learning over time.

Imagine what happens when a faculty or workplace mentor works with students or colleagues without much interaction and communication; when the faculty or mentor forgets to be 'with student'. An example of this is when, on one particular shift, I came on duty in the afternoon and found that the subordinate staff were very disgruntled. They were formulating a complaint to management about a senior manager that day. As their fellow colleague on the shift I listened to their angst and asked them why they just did not approach the person in question and tell them how they felt. They didn't feel they could. Having worked in this institution for some years and also carrying the Royal College of Midwives role of representing workers learning in the workplace, I had a healthy respect for all staff, including this particular member managing on that day. I felt the situation was one where the manager was working on automatic pilot; her huge amount of knowledge and experience had led her to believe she could run the shift alone and indeed this is exactly what was happening and the subordinate staff felt undervalued.

This is the problem with being unconsciously competent on one level; often you can work in a way that outwardly appears functional and the observer cannot see your expertise, just that things run smoothly for you while they struggle to fit in with you, not know what you are thinking and doing. This is what I call leaving the learner or colleague behind, being oblivious to their needs; your actions can almost appear robotic as you carry out the practical activities at such speed one wonders whether any thought processes are occurring. Robot or expert? An interesting question to consider. What was happening in this work situation? When I approached the midwife manager in question, speaking up for my colleagues, she was completely unaware that there were any issues and apologised for not working more as a team. She explained that she preferred to work in a way where she does everything, not leaving any duties except the very menial ones for other designated staff. Sometimes we feel it easier to do everything ourselves and not engage others because delegation itself takes time.

Following the discussions, the shift ended with everyone feeling much happier and a more cohesive working pattern ensued with the very competent senior being able to show off her expertise while acknowledging that she may have become unconsciously incompetent in that one particular area.

A midwifery teacher in the UK in the early nineties shared her exasperation with me, saying she could not understand how a midwife could practise for ten years and not change her skill level since year one – didn't update, wouldn't consider evidenced based practice – the midwifery teacher saw this attitude as one of thirty years of the first year of practice. In other words not changing from the skill level from the first year of qualification. Imagine remaining at a skill level for so long, not being motivated to improve practice.

Chapter 10

Tell them and they will know! Really?

Allowed to learn, allowed to know, but not allowed to do. I have long held the view that we are taught because the emphasis is on having knowledge, but that this is false because there are few people who 'do' or are allowed to 'do'. Many pretend they know something because they can recite something back and feel elated in that knowledge, assuming a certain level of authority because of this.

I have observed people teaching children numbers and because the child is able to rote recite the numbers back the adult feels elated that the child has learnt the numbers.

Piaget has written in depth about how children grasp numerical understanding in terms of numbers and quantity and also about child development. A basic knowledge of these theories would stop the nonsense of making children rote learn what is basically just a scripted number that does not help the child understand quantity or even be ready to understand these concepts. The same is true about making a child write the number when hand–eye coordination and understanding of quantities has yet to be developed. How does this relate to adult learning? Well it is about 'readiness to learn' also noted by adult learning (andragogy) theorists Knowles and Rogers and focuses on understanding concepts rather than the ability to recite a piece of text back verbatim!

I once struggled with challenging a teacher to really teach the student a concept; quite specifically it was about administering a particularly dangerous drug. I stated clearly that the outcome should be that they understand the drug and particularly its adverse effects; the teacher said to me that if they told them and they remembered, then they would know. To which I replied, really? I can understand how this 'telling' strategy is still evident in teaching practice.

Even as a teacher at the start of my career twenty-five years ago, I remember that the dictat was: 'tell 'em, tell 'em and tell 'em again'. We expected students to know and understand, just because we told them over and over again! Today I am passionate about learning by doing and thinking and really understanding the knowledge in practice. Studying work-based learning over the last ten years specifically has helped me to understand *how people learn how to do*, and *how to teach how to do and think*. Work-based learning is the best method to keep theory and practice closely aligned at all times. I will continue to study and undertake research in this field.

Much of this book hinges on the basic, fundamental learning needs of women and students. So I implore you as a teacher, don't pretend to teach, that is, *telling,* which is not teaching. As teachers we can be pressurised into focusing on the outcomes rather than on the process of learning. We seem to have moved away from learning for the purpose of being able to do, to a place where certificates (outcome) are important – certs, certs and more certs! Everything seems to have a competency as if all learning has been articulated and codified, when in fact most of what we do has not been written, because we are still discovering how people learn to do a skill and how someone actually becomes an expert. What is written is granted power and what is unseen and understood is diminished to second-class knowledge, even though being able to do something with skill should be revered.

While supporting undergraduates in a developing country they shared with me their frustrations of their final exam that merely expected them to recite textbook answers to a specific question rather than give examples from practice. The paper was set and marked by university teachers that hadn't practised in the workplace for a long time. Teaching and assessing in this manner supports the assumption that students are allowed to know, but not to do in reality. Perhaps it is because the educational institutions grade non-tacit and codified knowledge, themselves using the textbook to assess the final papers. A dilemma that affects every university in both developed and developing countries.

In contrast, I was once assisting an obstetrician supervising a learning doctor doing a minor operation and was amazed at how he drew practice knowledge out of the student; each time the student gave him a knowledge fact about something relevant to the operation, the obstetrician would loudly say: "show me". The operation lasted about thirty minutes during which time conversations were punctuated with 'show me, show me' followed by facial visual approval of the replies or coaxing till the correct justification of 'doing' was articulated by the student. Doctors are quite good at talking their thinking both from teacher to student and for assessment from student to teacher.

This example of reality teaching and assessing inspired me to carry on thinking and learning in my teaching practices – how I myself learn – and led me to question what education is about and who is it for.

Again, going back to my phrase 'allowed to know', I met one woman in a developing country who went through training that would help to reduce maternal mortality but shared with me that actually it was dirty work and her husband did not like her doing it. He worked for the funding organisation that paid for these programmes, but it seems they like to work in offices and claim they are a qualified health professional while never actually having practised. Knowledge, power and potential income generation sometimes dictates who can be 'told' (so say learn).

An example of this became obvious to me when, while supporting a train the trainer programme in a developing country, one of the midwifery teachers – a medical officer – advocated that student midwives and midwives should learn on simulators/dummies but not be allowed to touch her patients. It does not take much to realise that while patients pay for their care, simulators/dummies do not.

So the midwives are allowed to know but not really do because then they will earn money and possibly be in competition with those who want to keep the earning potential for themselves.

Sadly I see funding that should be targeted to train midwives ending up in the training and development needs of doctors who will never go to the areas where sixty per cent of women deliver without a skilled birth attendant. It is understandable that doctors invest a huge amount of money into their training and so expect a return on their investment both financially and with privileged status. Historically this idea of privilege practice showed that women, even in the United Kingdom during Victorian times, were not allowed to study medicine. In fact it was Scotland that allowed the first women ever to obtain a medical degree, and that doing of knowledge with gender differences in pay still prevails in the developed world today.

So on one hand you have a mass of people revering having knowledge as a status symbol and shunning the actual skill that goes with the knowledge; and then on the other hand you have money-conscious people that will continue to keep the expert knowledge and skill within a small section of the professional community so as to maintain power over the earning and status capacity. This is in spite of the fact that millions of women around the world need access to these skills and knowledge. This is what I refer to as abusing power and teachers can abuse their power by keeping students passive and not really teaching them so they can enjoy a certain level of status and employability themselves. Perhaps they don't want the student or junior teacher to know as much as them for fear they will no longer be needed.

The purpose of midwifery teaching is primarily to save millions of women's lives. This somehow gets forgotten in domestic, economic and institutional politics. Consider: is there is a very good reason to stick to traditional teaching methods because we may want to keep the student passive, stuck in their chair, and think that we have taught them because we have told them? To explain this, I once shared an example with a novice health care teacher. I said to her, repeat after me, 'C, A, T', which she did several times, probably three, just to be sure. At the end of this direct teaching method I said to her well done now you know everything about cats. I went on to explain that this is the problem with telling only. She never had the opportunity to see a picture of a cat or touch a real cat, but because I told her something she could then reveal she knew about cats.

This novice teacher felt that this was a good analogy of how telling is not teaching. Again, clearly the old adage about just telling is aptly put – in one ear and out the other.

Students become passive when you sit them in a chair and tell them, in the same way a healthy parturient woman becomes passive and perceives her state to be pathological when you put her in a bed. Just as I encourage midwives to mobilise the parturient woman, I encourage the midwifery teachers to mobilise the students. Their roles as they develop will require them to function autonomously both for the new mother and the new midwife. Consider what happens when you show the student – somehow finding a way to bring the concept to life – that you want to teach them. Recap your understanding of learners' needs here particularly with learner' styles; many students are visual learners some even having a well-developed photographic memory.

I discovered through trial and error myself that a group of students at any one time will focus on different aspects of a session, for example demonstration. I was demonstrating how to conduct the newborn's first examination by a midwife. I repeated the sequence twice and then asked each student to demonstrate back to me; while observing their actions I noticed that they missed out quite a few life-saving checks. So I decided to mime the examination once without explanation using exaggerated body and facial expressions and then asked each student to demonstrate back to me. I was amazed to find that their demonstration back to me was near perfect. This format was then followed by discussion into why the various examination techniques were important for improving mortality and morbidity rates of newborns.

This reminded me of the children's cartoon *Teletubbies* where a short video will be shown and then the bears say 'again, again' and the video is repeated. The reason for this is that children when viewing something will concentrate on the visual first time round and then the audio the second time round; repeated viewing allows them to piece the knowledge together to gain an understanding of what is going on. I believe adults are no different and process information with different senses at different times, which is why it takes so long to learn a skill. Bear in mind that showing is not enough; repetition and supervised practice in the real world is crucial.

I have been working with a group of midwifery teachers in a developing country over the last couple of years and while they are trying out these new teaching skills and getting the students out of their chairs I warned that they would not get good press to start with because students who have been inducted by traditional methods will expect to continue to be spoon-fed and expect knowledge to be given to them; it would take some time before the students could see that they were really developing skills and knowledge before positive feedback came their way. Interestingly this is the same with midwifery practice; while I have been teaching the midwives to protect normality, mobilise and hydrate their labouring women, they constantly send me reports that the women complain if they are not put in a bed with a drip and given an episiotomy; then they articulate they have not received good care. It seems that mobilising the labouring woman and student is going to take a little longer. Cultural and institutional norms may take ages to be delved into.

So, I have explored the problems with just telling and even just showing and now I want to recap involving: citing again the old adage, 'tell me and I will forget, show me and I may remember but *involve me and I will never forget'*. When you involve the student, this is learning by doing, preferably in the workplace. The ability to carry out a skill well could be said to be the consolidation of thinking and doing. This is where you can ask yourself whether you have really taught the students well? Have you tuned into their learning needs and facilitated a safe learning environment?

Much of this book has focused on real learning experiences which means that the student must be actively involved. Mobilise the student, talk your thinking to the student, allow the student to do, let go of the power and hand it back to the student. '**Telling is not teaching**', so... **Teach, Don't Tell.**

By Áine Alam Jan 2015

Further Reading

ICM Global Standards for Midwifery Education (2010 amended 2013)

ICM Global Standards for Midwifery Education – Companion Guidelines

ICM Global Standards for Midwifery Education – Glossary of Education Terms

ICM Essential Competencies for Basic Midwifery Practice (2010 amended 2013)

ICM Global Standards for Midwifery Regulation (2011)

ICM Model Curriculum Outlines for Professional Midwifery Education (2012)

ICM Standard Equipment List for Competency-Based Skills Training

ICM General Glossary for all ICM documents

http://sarah-stewart.blogspot.co.uk/2010/03/teaching-midwifery-students-about.html

http://www.who.int/maternal_child_adolescent/documents/9241546662/en/

https://teal.ed.gov/sites/default/files/Fact-heets/11_%20TEAL_Adult_Learning_Theory.pdf

http://www.internationalmidwives.org/assets/uploads/documents/Model%20Curriculum%20Outlines%20for%20Professional%20Midwifery%20Education/ICM%20Resource%20Packet%204%20Competency-based%20teaching%20&%20learning%20NEW.pdf

Funding from Wellbeing of Women supports the project of 'up-skilling midwives in Pakistan' from which this book evolved

WELLBEING
OF WOMEN

About Wellbeing of Women

Every woman born since 1964 will have benefited from research funded by Wellbeing of Women

Wellbeing of Women is a UK charity dedicated to improving the health of women and babies, to make a difference to people's lives today and tomorrow.

- We provide *information* to raise awareness of health issues to keep women and babies well *today*

- We fund pioneering medical *research* and *training grants,* which have and will continue to develop better treatments and outcomes for *tomorrow*

- Leading members of the medical profession including Lord Brain, Sir John Peel and Sir George Pinker founded the charity in October 1964. They were all very disturbed by the lack of scientific and medical research into the causes and prevention of abnormalities in pregnancy, childbirth, and gynaecology.

Members of the Wellbeing of Women Research Advisory Committee recommend the allocation of funds based on a robust peer review process, designed to ensure that only the best people and projects are selected. This process is on a par with those employed by the Medical Research Council and the Wellcome Trust. Our Research Advisory Committee is made up of twenty obstetricians, gynaecologists and other specialists. All of these experts serve three-year terms, thus ensuring up-to-date expertise across the specialities.

For 50 years, we have invested millions of pounds in funding the very best in medical research and training, resulting in some remarkable progress. Many of the early research projects we have funded are now a standard part of women's health care.

Wellbeing of Women is a member of the Association of Medical Research Charities

My Report to WOW February 2014

Up-skilling midwives in Pakistan IFA030

Inspired by RCM Global Midwifery Twinning Project

I am incredibly grateful for the Wellbeing of Women (WOW) IFA award which will be specifically used to fund field work and the dissemination of outputs of the project.

I am a UK practising midwife, health and social care educator, union learning representative for the Royal College of Midwives (RCM) and work-based learning (WBL) specialist.

In 2012 I was sent with two other British trained midwives to support midwifery in Uganda by the RCM. Our plan was in line with International Confederation of Midwives (ICM) agenda to tackle the high rates of maternal and infant mortality (Millennium Development Goals MDG 5 and 4) there. The plan had a three-pronged approach: 1) to support the midwives association, 2) to support education and 3) to support regulation.

Following this very valuable experience, in 2013 I read an article by Professor Rafat Jan about her endeavours to bring midwifery-led care back to Pakistan. I emailed her and shared my experiences and offered to go out and help.

Initially I was invited out to support the professional development of midwifery faculty at the Aga Khan University in Karachi and also to support the training of Pakistan's first midwifery degree students. I was also then involved with supporting the Midwifery Association of Pakistan and have met several times with the Pakistan Nursing Council including securing a licence to practise midwifery in Pakistan. This has meant that I have been able to influence association, education and regulation, a model which the RCM and ICM have for up-skilling midwives globally.

As I became more involved in this international work it became very clear to me that efforts to train midwives en masse were hampered by the lack of trained and skilled midwifery teachers. This alerted me to the possibility that inadequately trained midwives had the potential to actually increase maternal and infant morbidity not reduce it. Working very closely with faculty and practising midwives in both countries meant that the need to support midwifery-led care and midwifery-led teaching practices was crucial if MGD 4 and 5 were to be to be truly tackled. Midwifery teachers shared with me that they wanted to learn how to teach midwifery students and how to do midwifery in practical ways as opposed to 'chalk and talk' and endless PowerPoint presentations, which encompass traditional teaching methods that tell but don't really teach.

Having studied Work-Based Learning at Masters and currently PhD level, I was eager to take learning out of the classroom and into the real world of work. For one year over four visits to Pakistan I modelled practical teaching methods where faculty and students were encouraged to be proactive, to learn through simulation and supervised practice in the clinical areas. Interestingly all of these practice skills sessions (except clinical areas) were recorded on video and students photographed learning opportunities. Images were discussed in depth and sent on to midwifery colleagues throughout Pakistan via social networking media. I became interested in how it is that these midwifery teachers might adapt practical teaching methods that are fit for them in their context. With research supervision from my London-based Middlesex University, the WBL team designed a research method that would use multimedia as the main data collection tool, expanding really on a method that faculty and students use comfortably themselves. A theory of how people and objects of all sorts interact to form useful and effective happenings – or not – called Actor–Network Theory, guided the research design and will guide the very close examining of data to be collected. Refining the research method has taken over 18 months to ensure that the framework is sound and realistic. Data collection will begin late spring.

However my international work continues to look at the three-pronged approach as I continue supporting the Midwifery Association, education development and also regulation. An unanticipated output of the project has been the writing of a book to help the midwifery teachers. Early in my involvement I asked the midwifery faculty in both Pakistan and Uganda what they would like to see if I were to write them a long letter about teaching students 'how to do'. The book *Teach, Don't Tell*, asks midwifery faculty to take seriously their role in training midwives and reducing maternal and infant mortality. It shows the midwifery teachers how to mobilise and give power back to the student, aligned with mobilising mothers birthing their babies and giving power back to mothers too.

The examples in the book are based on my many years of teaching and specifically midwifery teaching in the international countries I have been involved with, so that the ideas fit with the needs of the midwife teachers there.

My project of up-skilling midwives in Pakistan has been further defined as 'the Practice Project' and forms my PhD studies, setting a firm focus that it is all about skills and in particular about how midwifery teachers teach student midwives how to do midwifery in safe and dignified ways.

The idea is that a small group of midwifery faculty who have been exposed to practical teaching methods video themselves teaching midwifery students how to practice midwifery. Then we will view the video clips together and our discussions of how they feel they are teaching and students learning will be recorded using an audio recorder. The midwifery curriculum and lesson planning documents and my researcher's field notes will form a third section of data collection. So that means there will be video observation, audio interviews and documentary evidence which will need thorough detailed examination to find out how these midwifery teachers adapt practical teaching strategies and how they feel about it.

This sequence will be repeated three times – at the beginning of a new midwifery degree programme, in the middle and then into its final year. This detailed descriptive research will be guided by my personal university supervision team ensuring that it's reputable and to an internationally accepted standard. This research is at an early stage and is expected to span several years.

This type of study, looking closely at how midwifery teachers teach using multimedia as a data collection tool, has not been done before. However, I have learned from reading other research, reports and articles from many other disciplines such as nursing, medicine and teaching that attempts to move away from traditional teaching methods to practice-based approaches have been fraught with difficulty and have resulted in limited success. My opinion here is that if the interventions and subsequent research were more aligned with the indigenous needs of the participants then success levels may have improved.

Optimistically I hope that my close engagement with midwifery faculty, students and midwives in Pakistan throughout the duration of my project will yield positive results in helping teaching and learning to move away from traditional teaching methods to one where the student is empowered to learn how to practise safe and dignified care for mothers and babies, indirectly impacting on maternal and infant mortality. I plan to disseminate the results in conferences and publications. Furthermore I will be encouraging faculty to conduct their own research and engage in scholarly writing.

Aside from PhD studies I have been involved in train the trainer programmes, which is where midwifery faculty and I have worked closely together to refine practical teaching methods that work for these particular teachers in their context. Last May the Midwifery Association of Pakistan held a large conference for more than 300 midwives where I presented an afternoon event on practical strategies to support normal labour. With this conference and the midwives and midwifery tutors, five-week residential workshops throughout Pakistan have meant that faculty and myself have engaged with more than 400 midwives and 60 midwifery tutors to drive home the importance of safe and dignified care using practical teaching methods. My work with Ugandan midwives and midwifery teachers also continues with a recent visit there in December 2014 working closely with curriculum development from certificate in midwifery to degree, through to Masters, instilling portfolio and practise development documents as assessment strategies to ensure that the focus is on practise through work-based learning. This last visit to Uganda concludes the end of the current GMTP for the RCM.

I would like to think that the standing of WOW in regards to this project may be elevated, demonstrating that supporting midwives and midwife teachers to venture out into areas of need can have a lasting impact in tackling MDGs 4 and 5. I hope that my book for midwifery teachers, stories and dissemination of results will encourage benefactors to donate more to WOW and for midwives to seek funding to demonstrate their passion of 'being with women' for safe and dignified care. I believe the way the funding was allocated (though difficult to access for me) shows transparency and will give benefactors confidence that their volunteer funds are appropriately awarded and monitored.

About the Author

Áine Alam is a practising midwife, teacher and researcher, specialising in midwifery-led care including water births and teaching practices that have a work-based learning focus. Áine holds qualifications in nursing, midwifery, advanced midwifery practice, clinical teaching and learning, assessor awards, teacher training, a Masters in work-based learning (WBL) and is currently pursuing sponsored PhD studies (WBL) about how midwifery teachers learn to teach midwifery skills.

Born in Ireland to a large family with 11 siblings, Áine currently lives in Kent, England with her husband and four children working as a midwife in the NHS, though presently on sabbatical in order to carry out her international research. Áine was awarded an International Fellowship Award from the charity Wellbeing of Women (WOW) in collaboration with the Royal College of Midwives (RCM).

Áine also volunteers as a learning representative for the RCM conducting learning events across London and Kent for midwifery colleagues. The RCM, funded by DFID, have twice placed Áine in Uganda to assist universities with their curriculum development for midwives, influencing how midwives will be taught and ensuring 'learning by doing' as opposed to lecture-led learning with the ultimate aim of reducing the vast number of mothers and babies who die in childbirth.

Contact Áine at: aine.alam@nhs.net

Lightning Source UK Ltd.
Milton Keynes UK
UKOW06f2257260615

254215UK00001B/3/P